MIRACLE FABRICS

MIRACLE FABRICS

BY
Ellsworth Newcomb
and Hugh Kenny

ILLUSTRATED BY
AVA MORGAN

G. P. Putnam's Sons
New York

To
Margaret and Bunny Dexter

In the research that has been necessary in the preparation of this book, the authors gratefully acknowledge the assistance of many organizations and individuals, including the following:

American Viscose Corporation
Celanese Corporation of America
E. I. du Pont de Nemours & Company
Glass Fibers, Inc.
National Cotton Council of America
Naugatuck Chemical Division, U. S. Rubber Co.
Union Carbide Corporation
The Wool Bureau, Inc.

CONTENTS

1: MILESTONES ALONG AN ANCIENT TRAIL

WHEN you look at your window curtains or your clothes or at any of the familiar things which are made of cloth, it is surprising to know that even if they were bought yesterday, their story began so long ago that there is no book old enough to tell the beginning of it. But this is true. Thousands of years ago, with the coming of the Ice Age, early man began to search for coverings to keep him from being frozen to death. Centuries later actual textile-making grew out of that first desperate search.

We do not know who the first clothmaker was. We do not know exactly when or where the first cloth was made. But from clues which we have, historians believe that the first "cloth" men ever had was woven cloth. We know, too, that after woven material began to take the place of the animal hides and "natural" felts —man's first clothing—almost all cloth was made of wool, silk, cotton and linen.

From the time man learned to weave he never stopped looking for fibers to spin into thread for his looms. In very early days he discovered these tiny strands, or fibers, on the backs of sheep, in the co-coons of insects or growing in fields. He learned how to spin them and make them into ropes, fishing nets, sails and cloth and many other things which helped him to live and progress.

Because wool, silk, cotton and flax come from ani-mals and plants, we call them and all other fibers sup-plied by nature, "natural fibers."

For many, many centuries the fibers which nature grew for us were the only ones we had. They were fine gifts and as the long years passed, people learned how to use them with more and more skill. They learned how to dye the cloth they made. They constantly im-proved their methods of weaving it and shaping it into clothes and other articles. Often the things they made were very beautiful.

But there was never enough precious silk to go around. Sometimes wool, linen and cotton were scarce, too. Also, in spite of his skill in handling them, man could not always make nature's fibers do exactly what he wished.

So at last man began to dream of a fiber that would always be plentiful and that could be made into a fabric that was warm or cool, strong or delicate, or whatever he needed for a particular use. But certainly no such ideal natural fiber existed on the face of the earth. Where could he hope to find it?

To find such a fabric seemed so nearly impossible that sometimes man's dream faded. Sometimes it seemed to be entirely forgotten. But throughout his history, man has put his intelligence to work to improve his way of life. The dream of an ideal fiber did not die, either. After many years scientists took a bold step toward making it come true. They began to try to copy nature. They began to try to create the ideal fiber themselves.

Today we are told we are still far from the end of the trail, although we now have so many different fibers it almost seems as if there must be one that is perfect for every imaginable need.

Tires for our automobiles, for example, must stand up under hard punishment. Our factories turn out extra-heavy-duty fibers that form the skeletons for rubber tires and for making other strong, strain-proof materials. The hawsers that haul barges and the rope that goes into the big cargo nets used in loading ships are made of special fibers. Still other fibers are manufactured for the safety belts of linesmen and others who work in dangerously high places and who must depend on fiber-strength for their very lives.

To make sheer stockings, pretty party dresses and dainty curtains, cobweb-thin material made from delicate fibers is needed. There is plenty of that, too, in our modern world. We also have fabrics that magically keep trouser creases just where they are meant to be; pleats that will stay in skirts; beautiful wool-like cloth that won't shrink when washed; curtains and car and furniture slip covers that need no ironing. We have fabrics that are warm—some look almost exactly like fur. We have fabrics that are cool. We have others that resist the hungriest moths and are even proof against mildew.

We know these many-purpose fabrics by such names as rayon, nylon, Orlon, Dacron, Dynel and so forth, or as "synthetics" (a word which means "put together"), or as partially synthetic.

They are all so plentiful and familiar that we can scarcely imagine how we would get along without them. Yet each one is a new and towering milestone along man's trail in search of textile fibers. And each was made possible by a recent marvel of human achievement. Instead of depending entirely on nature for his supply, man has learned to create fibers chemically.

This wonder of our laboratories, the chemically made fiber, is far more under man's control than the fibers which are found in nature. It is, in fact, of such great benefit to mankind the world over, that its discovery is a richer treasure than any oil or uranium find on earth.

That discovery came only after centuries of seeking. Much of the way was as hard and adventurous as a voyage of exploration. How the man-made fiber grew from a dream into what is now chemistry's largest industry is an astonishing chapter in the history of our progress.

But why is it surprising that science has found out how to make a fiber? Just what *is* a fiber, anyway?

An easy way to find out is to tear a little wad of absorbent cotton off the roll that can be found in almost every household medicine cabinet. Now keep pulling the wad apart until you can separate one small, thread-like strand from the others. That tiny bit of white is a natural fiber. It came from a living cotton plant.

Of course, by the time the absorbent cotton was made into a roll it had been combed free of seed, bleached and so forth, or what we call "refined." Its form, though, is basically the same as when it grew in some cotton field.

If we snipped a small wad of wool from a sheep's back, it, too, could be separated into minute fibers. If we also had bits of flax and silk we would see that, except for the great length of the silk fibers, all four of the principal natural fibers look very much alike to the naked eye.

When we are talking about fabrics, then, the word *fiber* means any tiny, sometimes almost invisible, strand which, combined with other strands, can be spun into yarn. Such strands also may be correctly called filaments, a word often used for the silkworm's long thread.

Actually it was the silkworm's wonderful four- to eight-hundred-yard-long filaments which scientists were trying to copy when they began the daring experiment of creating fibers. Later we shall hear about the many obstacles which had to be overcome before the very first of the man-made fibers began to be sold just before the beginning of our own twentieth century.

Today we call that first chemically created fiber, and the cloth made from it, rayon. Making it was a truly great achievement and many marvels have followed it. But still the centuries-old search for better fibers and fabrics goes on. Wonderful as our new fibers are, no one fiber has every quality which would make it ideal.

Nylon's remarkable elasticity, for example, makes it perfect for some things. But under certain conditions it does not feel comfortable. Dacron sheds water like a duck and holds creases obligingly. But it must be ironed with special care. Some otherwise excellent fibers will not dye well; others stick to perspiring bodies; still others give their wearers miniature electric shocks which are unpleasant.

So it is plain to see that there is still plenty of work to be done before anything like an ideal fiber becomes a reality. Perhaps when scientists finally reach the end of the long trail, they will achieve a perfect fabric by combining new man-made fibers with those nature gave us so long ago.

Meanwhile the manufacture of the fibers and fabrics that have already been developed has become the biggest job in the entire field of chemistry. Amazing, too, is the fact that while once there was no such thing as cloth in the whole world, today the textile industry, in one way or another, keeps one out of every five of all of the working people on earth busy.

Before we hear the story of how science learned to

create the fibers which are made into so many of our modern fabrics, let us turn the calendar far backward and find out more about how we came to have fabrics in the first place.

2: MAN'S OLDEST SKILL

THOUSANDS of years ago, when one of the Ice Ages began to hold much of the ancient world in its deadly grip, man knew fire only in some natural form, such as the lightning which from time to time set his forests ablaze. He had not learned to tame it and make it work for him. Yet when he was in danger of freezing to death, he had to find some way to keep warm. He had to find some kind of covering if he was to survive.

That time was so far back in the mists before history began that almost all we definitely know about it is that man did manage to stay alive. From certain clues which various sciences have given us, however, we can guess, with some hope of being right, how people did get those first coverings—and how, in getting them, they may even have stumbled upon the principle that centuries and centuries later would be used in making cloth.

In the first place, we can be quite sure that early

man kept no record of passing months or years. Yet reason tells us he must have known something of the seasons. At least he must have noticed that the winter's cold softened into spring, and that spring was followed by summer warmth. Then came the autumn winds. We can picture him taking this familiar cycle for granted.

Then the pattern changed. Something alarming happened to the weather. Summer came too late to ripen the wild fruit. The mountaintops, usually covered with grass at this time of year, were instead blanketed with snow.

More frightening still, a band of wild strangers began to straggle down from the white mountain peaks. They made known by signs that they were hungry. But because of the late-coming summer, food was scarce even in the lower lands we are picturing. When the strangers tried to stay, the older inhabitants frantically drove them away to starve or freeze.

The hungry mountain people were no longer a danger. But now as the days grew shorter, the long nights were terrifyingly cold. Then a tiny greenish dot was seen between the hills. It grew and grew into a huge sheet of glacial ice that inched down into the valley, pushing giant rocks ahead of it. Ice, mud and granite thundered down, and mammoth trees were splintered into sticks.

Then the snow began to fall.

It snowed for days and weeks and months. While

man looked on, shivering and frightened, more and more snow whirled down. It covered the tracks of the animals which were racing southward, instinctively seeking the sun. As their snow-muffled feet hurry away, let's look at one of those terrified, starving, half-frozen men who were on earth when the Ice Age began.

He is thickset and, to our eyes, quite an ugly creature. His looks frighten us, yet we can't help but pity him, shivering there in his ruined world, a scowl darkening his face. Suddenly his eyes brighten. He has caught sight of a huge bear lumbering over the white ground.

To Ice Age man, the bear meant but one thing— food. Clumsily he lunged after the animal. But a few feet beyond his reach it suddenly vanished.

When he got over his surprise, our primitive hunter edged closer to the place where the bear had disappeared. He wanted to know what had become of it. As he drew nearer he saw a deep hole almost hidden by snow-covered leaves and branches. Inside it the bear crashed around, wildly struggling to climb back to freedom. But the hungry hunter found a heavy stone, aimed it and put a quick end to the bear's struggles.

That night our Ice Age man and his family ate raw bear meat. Then they huddled under the bear's furry hide and found that it gave them a little shelter from the bitter cold.

The bear meat did not last long, though. Early man soon needed more meat to feed his family and more

animal hides to shield them from the terrible weather.

From time to time bears and hyenas crashed through the wrecked forest in their search for the sun. But early man was an awkward creature, and he had wandered so far away from the hole that had trapped the bear for him that he could not manage to catch another animal. His mind was almost as clumsy and slow as his body. But at last there came a day when he had to use his brain or die.

Slowly, painfully, he began to try to copy the hole that had saved him and his family. Hour after hour he clawed at the hard ground. Finally there was quite a large hole. But he knew there was something missing. Then he remembered the branches that had hidden the other hole from the bear. He tried to hide the one he had made in the same way, but the branches were blown off time after time. At last, to keep them in place he poked and tucked a second set of branches in among the first set, so that in a very crude way the two sets were interwoven.

As he waited, out of sight behind a rock, for some animal to plunge down into the pit he had dug, our Ice Age man did not know that he was making something besides his trap. For the interlacing, or interweaving, of branches in some such way as we have imagined is thought to have been the first clumsy step toward weaving—probably the very oldest of all man's crafts.

It was a long, long time, however, before anyone thought of using that same interlacing method to weave strands into cloth.

As the centuries passed, man went on using animal skins for warmth—and very likely he often wore them because he liked the way he looked in them, too. In some parts of the world people discovered that such creatures as sheep, camels and goats shed masses of hair. When they lay on it, it became matted down into something a little like what today we call felt. It was the duty of the last man in any caravan to gather up this "natural" felt, which was highly valued and was used as a fabric for a long time. It may have been this matted hair that gave primitive people the idea for another kind of cloth that they made later in their history. This was made by soaking a certain sort of tree bark in water until it became a pulp. Then heavy mallets were used to beat, or "felt," the fibers into a flat mat, pressing out the water at the same time. Later, when dry, the fibers would be locked together, just as they are in the paper of the page which you are reading.

Evidently, though, that way of interlacing branches that may first have been used to trap animals was never entirely lost. And it may be that people were reminded of it again when they began to make felt from bark. For the inner fibers of some trees and plants are so closely interwoven that they form a sort of natural cloth.

Before he began to weave cloth, man wore felt produced by animals and felt made from tree bark. He had mastered the principle of weaving even earlier, however. Sometime during the Old Stone Age of his progress, when he learned to make stone implements, he began to weave branches to make mats, and baskets which he lined with clay. He set the baskets over the fires which by this time he had also found out how to build. The baskets, of course, burned away, but pieces of the clay linings have been found with the weaving pattern baked into them.

Around that time, too, man found that by driving sticks into the ground and lacing branches and vines back and forth among them, he could make shelters

from the wind. By the time the New Stone Age began, some ten thousand years ago, he had discovered how to join the sides of such shelters, or windbreaks. Then, by plastering the sides with mud and adding a roof, he made a little woven house to take the place of the caves he had lived in for so many generations. This method worked so well that thousands of years later, in 55 B.C., when Caesar conquered England, he found people living in houses made in that very way.

Back in the New Stone Age, fish traps and beds and many other things were made by the interlaced branch method, too. But no matter how skillfully they were woven, such stiff, scratchy materials as vines and branches could not possibly be made into clothes.

Before the people of those ancient times could weave cloth, they had to have strands of something fairly soft and pliable. But nothing of the kind they needed could be found ready for use anywhere in nature. They had to make it for themselves. They had to take some of the things which nature gave them and make them into yarn. They had to learn to spin.

In the language of clothmaking, to spin usually means to twist short fibers together in order to make one long, sturdy strand. After such a strand is spun it may correctly be called either yarn or thread.

No one knows just when or where the first of this kind of spinning was done. But we do know that this art, too, was learned sometime during the New Stone Age. Perhaps bits of wool torn from sheep as they scrambled through thorny underbrush gave man the idea. He may have twisted the fleecy locks together into a strand to use instead of the animal sinews and plant fibers, such as hemp and jute, which he used as fastenings.

But whether or not wool was the first fiber ever to be spun, it is a fact that wool, silk, flax and cotton were all used for making yarn a very long time before the first history was written.

We cannot know exactly how the people of those early days went about turning nature's fibers into yarn, or thread. It is almost certain, however, that the first spinning was done without tools of any kind. Then, gradually, simple tools came to be used. Now in our modern times complicated machinery has taken their place, but it does the same basic work that was done by those primitive tools.

With weaving it is much the same story. For if we look at our giant power looms we see that they, too, must take the same essential steps that were taken by their early ancestors.

To find out how man's oldest craft has developed through the ages, let's go to call on a young girl, a spinner in one of the ancient lake villages of England.

3: SPINNING AND WEAVING

WE ARE now going to pretend that we are back in one of ancient England's lake villages watching one of the villagers at the work of spinning. We must remember, though, that the pretty young girl we are about to meet was not the first person ever to spin fibers into thread. As we have already learned, the very first spinning was undoubtedly done without tools of any kind. When we look closely at our lake-village spinner, we find that she has some simple tools.

For example, tucked into the girdle, or belt, of her wool dress is a forked stick called a *distaff,* on which a loose bundle of wool has been wound. The girl also has a second stick which is weighted at one end. This is a *spindle.*

Weights from such spindles have been found in earth that has not been disturbed for eight or ten thousand years. From these and other finds, we know that tools for spinning and weaving go back to the New Stone Age.

DISTAFF

CARDS

SPINDLE

Before such tools were invented, human fingers had to rake and comb the burrs and trash out of the raw wool fibers and make the fibers lie almost parallel. That early step in the clothmaking process is called *carding*. Crude hand combs were the first tools for this job; today machines do it for us.

The next operation in those ancient times was also done without tools. The spinner patiently pulled the short fibers out and twisted them together into finished thread, which she then wound on a stick. One day perhaps some spinner dropped her stick by accident, with the thread attached to one end. Since she was holding the thread, the stick hung in mid-air. The weight of the stick pulling on the newly made thread began to untwist the fibers, giving the stick a rotary motion like a top. Watching this, she caught the stick with her free hand to stop the untwisting. Then, turning it back again, she found she could make a foot or more of thread at a time, a good deal faster than she could twist the fibers together with her fingers alone. It may be that in this way the spindle was invented.

Anyhow, such simple tools as the distaff and spindle gradually came to be used. Most of the credit for their invention belongs to women. For it was the girls and women who during many centuries did almost all of the spinning and weaving of the world.

Nowadays a great many men are also engaged in this vast industry, and countless changes have taken place. Yet to this very day, thread is produced by means of the same basic steps that were taken by our lake dweller thousands of years ago.

Before we find out what those steps were, though, it will be interesting to know a little about the place that was our prehistoric spinner's home.

We have called it a lake village and, odd as that may sound, that is exactly what it was: a small group of tiny huts or houses which usually were built on stilt-like poles that stuck up out of shallow water or marshes. These strange villages were first built during the New Stone Age, and it is largely because scientists have been able to study their remains that we have some knowledge of the Europe of that long-past era.

We know, for example, that the lake dwellers were peace-loving farmers who chose their island-like homes because of the protection the water gave them, their families and their domestic animals. The watery location also made it easy for the lake villagers to fish and to go by boat to neighboring communities. Sometimes there were as many as fifty villages in the same lake.

But let's return to the village where our spinner lives and pay a visit to her house. We have named our young friend Neo because that is the first part of the archeologists' word "neolithic," which is a combination of two Greek words: *neo* (new) and *lith* (stone).

After herding their flock of sheep into the water so that the wool will be cleaner, Neo's father and her brothers have sheared off the animals' fleece with crude knives, probably made of sharpened stone. By the time we arrive, the men have brought great piles of wool into the house. Perhaps Neo would like to be outdoors, fishing or going by boat to a friend's house. But of course there were no shops in the world of that ancient New Stone Age. Every single thing the lake dwellers ate or wore or used for any purpose had to be supplied by the villagers themselves. Each day there were many, many jobs to be done. Right now Neo's job is to prepare the valuable wool for weaving into clothes and other necessities.

Before we met her, she had already done part of the work. With a piece of leather into which a good many big, tough thorns had been stuck (it looked somewhat like a brush with thorns instead of bristles) Neo had brushed and brushed a lot of the raw wool until all the brambles and snarls were out of it and all of the fibers lay fairly evenly in the same direction.

This is the process of carding which you read about at the beginning of this chapter. Although it is at least eight thousand years old and is now done in a different way, carding is still one of the first steps in making raw wool into thread or yarn.

Once Neo had carded some of the wool, she formed it into loose rolls called *slivers*. She tied these to a kind of forked stick which is the distaff you also read about earlier.

Next she tucked the distaff into her belt so that her hands were left free to pull out and slightly twist the slivers. She is finally ready to spin. She pulls out an end of the sliver until she has about a yard of loosely twisted, stringlike wool, called a *roving*.

Now she is ready to use that very important spinning tool, the spindle. As we know, it is also a stick. But instead of being forked like the distaff, the spindle is straight and one end of it is weighted by a stone or a piece of baked clay. This makes it heavy enough so that when Neo gives it a twist it will spin at an even speed and will have enough power to do the work she wants it to do.

With quick, practiced fingers Neo ties the loose end of her yard-long roving to a notch cut into the top of her spindle. While she holds onto her roving with one hand she gives the spindle a twist between the thumb and forefinger of her other hand and lets the spindle drop into the air. Now, because of its weight as it hangs suspended, the spindle whirls around and around, twisting the attached roving into thread. This kind of quite even and tight twisting together of fibers into yarn or thread is called spinning.

To find out how a spindle works, unwind the strands of a piece of string. Fasten one end of the string to a small stone or weight of some kind. Now, while you hang onto the unweighted end, let the weighted end fall free. The separate strands of your string will twist up again nearly as tight as they were before you separated them. But you will have to give your weight a twirl to get the fibers all the way back to their original position.

Some people think that the very first toy top was a real spindle which a mother of long ago gave her child for a plaything. We cannot be sure of that or of just how the first spindle came to be made. But, like the carding tool and the distaff, although it dates back so far into the past a spindle of some kind is even today an absolutely necessary tool in making thread from natural fibers.

Back in her queer little house surrounded by water, Neo has now spun a yard of raw wool into yarn. What will she do with it?

Her next step is to wind the finished yarn onto the spindle just above the weight, or *whorl* as it is often called. When she has fastened the yarn there, she draws out and loosely twists another length from the mass of wool on her distaff. Then she twirls and drops her spindle again. It twists up another yard of roving into thread. Again she winds and fastens the finished piece on her spindle.

Over and over Neo repeats these steps until a quantity of raw wool has been spun and her hard work for that one day is done.

After a good many more days of spinning, Neo's family will have enough thread for the loom which will weave it into cloth. It is likely that linen, also, will be woven in Neo's household, for flax as well as wool was grown and used by the lake villagers.

Just as the spindle and the distaff are major spinning tools, the loom is a major device for weaving. It, too, has a history that is very ancient. For, almost as soon as primitive people learned how to spin thread for cloth they must have had to find some way to fasten the threads that often became a hopeless tangle when they tried to weave, as they had once spun, with their hands alone.

Probably the first attempt at a loom was no more than a tree limb or a roof to which some weaver fastened her up-and-down threads in order to leave her hands free for weaving the crosswise threads in and out among them. But if you were to tie several lengths of string to a horizontal limb or tack them to the edge of your roof, you can imagine how the first breeze that came along would tangle the loose ends. Even though the method left your hands free, it would be hard work to intertwine any crosswise string with that snarled up-and-down set.

The first weaving was done on makeshift looms of that kind, but making cloth in such a crude way certainly must have been a problem.

Then some weaver found a fairly good solution. She weighted the loose ends of her up-and-down threads with stones or lumps of clay. Along with spindle whorls, some of these centuries-old weights have been discovered and they are among our best clues to the ancient past. Weighted in this way, the up-and-down threads stayed in place much better, while the crosswise threads were woven in and out among them.

Slowly, as time passed, frames came to be built for the special purpose of holding one set of threads in a

fixed position, so that a second set could be woven through them far more easily. The earliest of such frames was the first real loom. No one knows when or where or by whom it was invented. It has been dust now for unnumbered ages. Yet it was the first of all the instruments actually built in order to make possible one of mankind's most fundamental arts—that of weaving.

The descendants of that first loom are huge and complicated. But since so much of the story of modern as well as ancient textiles involves this art which goes back beyond the beginning of written history, let's take the time to find out what weaving is.

Do you recall reading earlier how a man of the Old Stone Age put sticks in the ground in order to make a shelter? Well, those upright sticks can be compared to the set of up-and-down threads which are held in place by a loom. The up-and-down threads are called *warp* threads or yarns. They always run the long way of woven cloth. Stretching the up-and-down warp threads on a loom is the very first step in weaving.

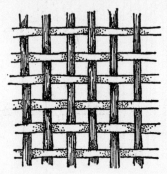

You remember, too, that when the Old Stone Age man built his shelter he did it by twining branches in and out at right angles to the upright sticks. In weaving, the threads that run crosswise, as those branches did, are called the *weft* (sometimes the woof) or filling threads, or yarns. Weft threads always run crosswise of woven cloth, and they run from side to side and back again in one long, continuous thread. The crosswise, weft threads are not fastened to the loom. They are threaded in and out among the warp yarns which hold them in place.

This over-and-under crossing of the warp by the weft threads is what is meant by weaving. As you can see, it is much the way the man of the Old Stone Age intertwined branches among his upright sticks.

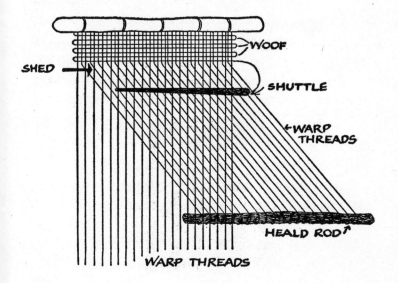

If you have ever watched your mother darn a sock you have seen a form of weaving. For undoubtedly she sewed a number of parallel threads across the hole in the sock and then ran more threads in and out among those first ones at a right angle to them.

In darning, the sock itself acts as a kind of frame or loom.

The first weavers no doubt ran the weft threads in and out among the warp threads one at a time, exactly the way the Old Stone Age branches were woven. This was slow and tedious. Some unknown weaver, looking for a quick way, thought of tying each alternate thread to a horizontal stick. Then, by moving the stick toward him, he could move half the threads at once. This formed a kind of tunnel of threads like the tunnel you can look through when you interlace the tips of the fingers of one hand with the tips of the fingers of your other. Through this tunnel of threads the weaver could then pass the weft thread, which would unwind from another stick as he moved it. This stick is called the *shuttle*.

The stick to which the first, third, fifth, etc., warp threads are tied is called the *heald rod*. The passage between two sets of warp threads is called a *shed*.

All of these important improvements in the art of making cloth came about before written history began. Then finally, about fifty-five hundred years ago, man's social and material well-being had reached a level so high that he was no longer primitive. Slowly and painfully humanity had progressed to a better, more ordered way of life which we call civilization.

After the gradual dawning of this new period still more advances, of course, continued to be made in many skills, including spinning and weaving. In India the spinning wheel (which we shall hear more about later) was invented to hasten the process of twisting fibers into thread. In China better looms were made which, along with some in Egypt, produced fabrics of such wonderful quality that they have never been surpassed. But except for a few improvements, thousands of years were to pass with very little change taking place in the method of making cloth or in the speed or skill of its production.

Then quite early in the eighteenth century a curious thing happened. A modest little plant which we know as cotton helped to change greatly the entire fabric-making process.

A queer kind of race between spinners and weavers was started when, in 1733, an Englishman named John Kay invented the fly shuttle, the principle of which is still one of the most important in modern mechanical weaving. The story of how that race helped to set off the world-wide change to machine power which we call the Industrial Revolution is one of adventurous spirits backed up by knowledge, hard work and determination.

Before we hear about it, however, we shall want to know something about the two major textile fibers from the vegetable kingdom—flax and cotton.

4: FLAX FROM PLANT TO FABRIC

FROM the time man first learned to spin, he has searched the world for textile fibers. The long list of materials which have actually been woven includes such curious things as feathers, hair, skin, metal and even rock.

But—until the quite recent discovery that he could make fibers chemically—of all the natural fibers man tried to use, four proved to be far the best suited to his purposes. These were flax, cotton, wool and silk —the first two from the vegetable kingdom, the others from the animal kingdom. For many centuries these four gifts from nature had no serious rivals.

Of this important group, the flax plant, from which linen is made, is certainly one of the oldest. During the Old Stone Age flax was used to make fishing nets and lines, animal traps, and cords for carrying things. Later on, as we know, the lake villagers wove both flax and wool, and possibly it was flax which they first wove into cloth.

Whether or not linen is older than wool fabric, however, we probably know more details of its production in early times than we do of any other. For this knowledge we must thank the Egyptians, who founded the first of all the great civilizations. For, on the walls of

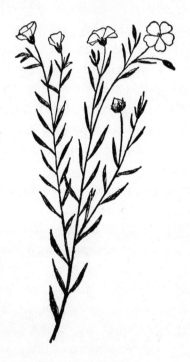

the tombs where the rulers of this ancient people were buried, the Egyptians described in pictures just how they grew flax and made it into beautiful linen five thousand years ago.

Luckily these records have lasted through the centuries and have been brought to light by archeologists and others. By studying them, we can follow each step in the production of linen from the sowing of the flax seed to the weaving of the cloth.

One of the strangest things the tomb pictures show is that as the Egyptians planted their precious flax seed they used oxen, sheep and goats to trample it down into the plowed earth with their sharp hoofs. We learn, too, that the seed was sowed very thickly so as to crowd the plants and make them grow tall and thin. This clever way of planting was deliberately used so that the fibers inside the flax stems would be long and fine. When the flax stalks were about two feet tall they bore pretty blue flowers and soon formed seeds. When the crop was around two months old the first harvesting was done by slaves.

Unlike most plants, flax was—and still is—harvested by pulling the entire plant up by the roots instead of cutting it. This is because if the stems were cut the fibers would be stained and could never be bleached enough to make pure white cloth.

Pulling flax on a scorchingly hot day was a very hard job, even for Egyptian slaves who were used to such tiring work. Yet this way of harvesting was used until, in our own times, machines were at last invented to do the back-breaking work of flax-pulling.

What would the overworked people of the Nile have said if they could have looked ahead five thousand years to see textile fibers not only being "grown" in the test tubes of our modern factories, but being produced in such great quantity and variety as they are today?

Back in those early days of civilization, pulling instead of cutting was not the only odd thing about harvesting flax. The Egyptians also divided the harvest into three separate stages—each one for a different use.

The first plants were pulled up when the stems were still green, so that the fibers inside them were so soft they could be spun into the very finest thread. This thread was woven into beautiful white robes for the rulers and nobles. Several days later, when the stems of the plants which still stood were yellow, a second and larger lot was pulled. By that time the fibers within the stems were tough enough to make thread for sturdy, plainer clothes. When the stems were fully ripe the season's final crop of flax was pulled. The fibers of this third crop were so tough they were used for the coarsest linen to clothe the slaves, and to make such things as ropes and mats. Seeds from this crop were also gathered and carefully saved for the next year's planting time.

The tomb records show that flax was prepared for spinning in a slow, difficult way. But even after thousands of years the slaves of our own President George Washington still used the same age-old method. To this day in many parts of the world, steps identical with those of the Egyptians are followed.

Since up until the end of the eighteenth century flax was the most important of the vegetable fibers, let us have a quick look at the old way of getting it ready for spinning.

First of all, the flax seeds are shelled off by drawing the stems through a sort of comb which has teeth so fine the seeds cannot pass through it. This combing is called *rippling*. When it has been done, the flax is made into bundles which are set in the sun to ripen. Next the ripened bundles are put to soak in pits of water. This step, called *retting,* rots the hard stems away from the fibers. After two weeks or so of soaking, the flax is taken out of the pits, washed in fresh water and spread out to bleach and dry. By now there are only small pieces of flax still sticking to the inner fiber. To remove them, the flax is spread on flat stones and pounded with heavy mallets. After this pounding—called *scutching*—the flax fibers, which are about eighteen inches in length, are silky-smooth. When they have had a final combing, the slow months of sowing, harvesting and preparing are at an end. The flax fibers are at last ready to be spun into thread.

The Egyptian way of spinning flax was not exactly like that used by our prehistoric lake dweller, Neo, when she spun wool. The Egyptian spinner twisted flax fibers into a roving by rolling them between the palm of her hand and her thigh, and as she did this she kept adding new fibers and winding the loose roving into a ball. When the ball was big enough it was put in water so that the damp fibers stuck together easily as they were spun. (Today cotton thread is kept moist on the spinning machines of our modern factories.)

Just like Neo, though, the Egyptian spinner fastened one end of her roving to her spindle. Then she let the spindle fall and tightly twist her roving into good, strong thread. Next, when the spindle stopped whirling, she, too, wound her finished thread above the weight, or whorl, and secured it there before she twisted out more roving. She repeated these steps until her ball of roving was spun.

After it was wound off the spindles into skeins somewhat like those you see in yarn shops today, the thread was again bleached. Finally it had to be starched to keep it from being torn by the shuttle.

Now Egypt's treasured thread was ready for the loom which would turn it into linen cloth so fine it has never been surpassed in all history. The time had come for the task which took the greatest skill in the entire process. For you remember that, between New Stone Age days and those of the ancient Egyptians, what we call civilization had come about and man's skills and tools had greatly improved. As often happens, however, improvements and refinements had brought complications with them. The simple, warp-weighted loom of the lake villagers, for example, had been perfected until even the most ordinary loom in Egypt had two bars, or beams, which held the warp threads apart. One of these beams was called the *cloth beam,* the other the *warp beam*. When the warp threads between the two beams had been interwoven with the weft threads, the finished length of cloth was rolled onto the cloth beam. Then a new length of warp thread was unrolled from the warp beam to take its place and the weaving was continued.

The task that took more skill than anything else in the linen-making process was the winding of hundreds of fine warp threads on the warp beam. To find out what hard, patient work that winding was, try to count the number of threads that run the long way of a piece of cloth. These up-and-down warp threads run parallel to the smooth edge that you'll find will not ravel even though it is not hemmed. (This edge is the selvage or self-edge. It is formed on each side of woven fabric as the continuous weft, or filling thread, travels back and forth across the loom.)

Make a pencil mark an inch away from the selvage and count the threads between the selvage and the mark. You will feel as if you had counted a great many threads in just that one inch of cloth. But you will not have equaled the score of the finest linen of ancient Egypt by a long way. Some of the very finest Egyptian linen that has been found in the tombs has as many as 540 warp threads to the inch. When you know that some of the old looms were sixty inches wide you can appreciate the work of winding 32,400 threads on a warp beam.

Like the looms of the lake villagers, those in Egypt also had heald rods to which alternate warp threads were fastened. The lifting of the heald rod parted the two sets of threads in the same way, too.

But the civilized people of the Nile had added a very important tool to their weaving equipment. By this time a sort of case was used to enclose the stick on which the weft threads were wound. The name of this case is a *shuttle*. Held in the weaver's hand, this shuttle carried the crosswise weft thread smoothly through the opening, or shed, between the two sets of warp threads. Then the weaver lifted another heald rod and once again carried the shuttle through. To make the linen firm, each time the weft thread traveled across the loom it was pushed up tight against the one before it with a long piece of wood sometimes known as a *weaver's sword.*

In Mesopotamia, the country we now know as Iraq, linen was also woven. In fact, the flax plant or *linum,*

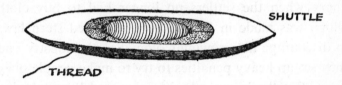

SHUTTLE

THREAD

as the Latins called it, has been grown there and in Assyria, too, for at least four or five thousand years. Probably the Finns introduced flax to Northern Europe, and later, it is thought, the West Aryans and the Phoenicians took it to Western Europe.

Long, long afterward when English colonists came to America, they grew flax from seed they brought with them. They prepared it for spinning in the same way that had been used by the Egyptians five thousand years before. In Colonial times, however, the spinner had a wheel to help her spin her thread. Colonial looms had also improved so much that some had as many as twelve *harnesses* which acted like heald rods and made it possible to weave a number of different patterns.

In 1607 when the first settlers came to Jamestown, they brought a few sheep with them. The tiny flock was carefully tended, and it increased so well that by the time the first American textile factory was built, there was home-grown wool to combine with home-grown flax in order to weave a very useful fabric called "linsey-woolsey." You can still see quilts and curtains of this linen-and-woolen cloth in some of our museums and historic old houses.

The English who ruled us in Colonial times became angry when the settlers no longer had to buy cloth which was made in England. They passed stern laws to discourage the growing Colonial cloth industry and they set up heavy penalties to try to make people obey them. But the brave colonists answered by producing more textile materials than ever. By 1776, when they finally declared their independence, they could supply themselves with fabric made from wool and from flax, and they even had some Georgia-grown silk and a little cotton.

Nowadays when cotton is so widely grown in the United States (and in many other countries) it may seem odd that the early settlers grew so little of it. But cotton thrives in warmer locations than those settled by the first colonists and, for other reasons we shall hear later, it was for a long time harder to work with than some of the other fiber plants.

So it was that flax kept on being the favorite and most important vegetable fiber until almost the end of the eighteenth century. Then, as we shall see, it was crowded out of its high place.

Today, though, machinery invented in Canada during the First World War and some invented later have made flax much cheaper and easier to harvest and clean. The plant is now profitably grown in Belgium, Ireland, the United States and numbers of other places, and linen is still one of the most popular fabrics we get from nature.

What was it that after so many centuries finally took flax's place as the major vegetable fiber? Perhaps you have already guessed that the answer is cotton—the very same little plant that our early settlers had slighted.

In the next chapter you will read about some strange and desperate adventures that are all part of the story of cotton.

5: COTTON BUILDS AN EMPIRE

WE HAVE had a hint of the important part cotton has had in the textile drama. But its importance is not a thing of the past. Today, fibers from this little plant, which is a relative of our familiar garden hollyhock, are the most used of any in the world. Not only are they made into cotton cloth, but countless pounds of the short ones are used in manufacturing some of our leading man-made fabrics.

Like the story of other natural textile fibers, no one can say just when that of cotton began. We do know, though, that three thousand years ago in India the weaving of cotton was already a very old craft.

Far back in the search for fibers (which is still going on at this moment), someone probably found cotton growing wild and was tempted to try to spin it. Somewhere along the line the experiment succeeded splendidly, for in very early times India's cotton cloth was of great beauty and value.

Later on, use of the fabric spread to the Mediter-

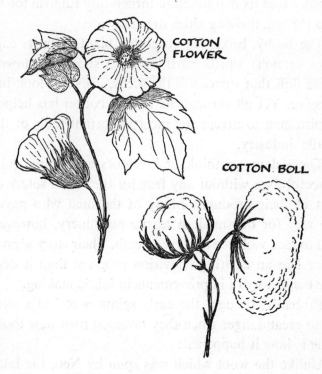

COTTON FLOWER

COTTON BOLL

ranean countries. In the first century A.D., it found its way over the trade routes to Italy and Spain. In the ninth century the Moors taught the Spaniards how to raise the plant, and we know that cloth made from cotton was woven there and in Venice and Milan hundreds of years ago. In our Western Hemisphere, the ancient Peruvians and Mexicans knew how to make cotton cloth which is so fine it looks like that found in Egyptian tombs.

But not until late in the twelfth century did cotton reach England, where it was one day to become so popular that its manufacture turned tiny English towns into the big, thriving cities they now are.

The bushy, broad-leaved cotton plant, with its capsules or bolls which burst open to show the downy white fluff that surrounds the seeds, does not look impressive. Yet all through its history cotton has helped inspire men to invent the most important tools of the textile industry.

These days we think of inventors as leading quite peaceful lives without any fear for their own safety or that of their products. Many of the men who paved the way for our modern textile machinery, however, had to face violence and even death. Their story sounds more like an exciting television program than it does like the history of improvements in fabric-making.

Probably, though, the early spinners of India were in no great danger when they invented their new tools. This is how it happened:

Unlike the wool which was spun by Neo, the lake-village girl, cotton fibers have no scales to make them cling together. Also, they are finer and shorter than flax fibers. This meant that in India workers could not spin cotton with the same kind of spindle that was used for either wool or flax. To work with cotton they had to think of a new way of spinning.

They made a smaller spindle and set it in a bowl of water to keep the cotton fibers damp enough to make them cling. Finally someone had the wonderful idea of fastening the spindle to a wheel. This invention was, of course, the now familiar spinning wheel, which we have all seen in pictures or in museums. When it was copied and improved upon in Europe during the fourteenth century it gave the world one of the great advances in thread-making and took the textile craft a long stride forward.

Hundreds of years ago in India a new loom, too, was invented—one with several harnesses to lift different sets of warp threads by means of foot pedals. The cotton cloth woven on these looms was much lighter and finer than any we now have.

More famous than these filmy cottons, though, were the brightly colored prints of India. These elaborately patterned cottons became the fashion in England, where they were first used as curtains and bedspreads and later for dresses. When the prints got to be so popular that they threatened to take the place of silk and wool, the English government passed a law against their use. But women went on wearing their rainbow cottons even when jealous woolen workers tried to rip them off their backs.

Since cotton prints were so popular, it was natural that some clever Englishman should try to imitate the foreign cloth. Soon fairly good English copies of it were on the market and orders poured in faster than they could be filled.

But it was not easy for English workers to use cotton on their spinning wheels and looms. So once again it was necessary to think of new and better methods. How they were invented is a remarkable story.

You remember that when one set of warp or up-and-down threads is lifted from another set, the space between the two is called the shed. It had always been a slow process for a weaver to pass the shuttle carrying the weft, or crosswise thread, from side to side of the loom through the shed.

In 1733, John Kay, an English weaver, worked out a way to operate his shuttle mechanically instead of by passing it from his right to his left hand and back again. Since Kay's amazing device darted back and forth faster and farther than any human hand, almost as if it were flying, it was named the *fly shuttle*. This shuttle was one of the most important improvements in all clothmaking history. Yet textile workers bitterly opposed the use of the invention.

"Kay's fly shuttle will take our places at the looms," the weavers roared. "We'll starve to death."

They destroyed the inventor's model, attacked his home, and would have killed Kay if a friend had not come to his rescue. The poor man escaped to France, where he later died as penniless as the angry weavers had pictured themselves.

John Kay was only the first of the Englishmen who had to risk violence because of their ideas for greatly improving clothmaking. His fly shuttle, however, was put to work. Equipped with it, faster-operating looms used up thread so fast that the spinners could not keep up with them.

Then one day, we are told, another Englishman, James Hargreaves, found his spinning wheel knocked over on its side with the spindle still whirling. Hargreaves stared at it. "Why, in that position," he exclaimed, "a wheel could turn more than one spindle. It could turn a dozen."

Fortunately Hargreaves had both the knowledge and the determination to turn an accident into a major achievement. In 1770, after three years of hard and secret work, he patented his new spinning machine, which he called the *spinning jenny* in honor of his small daughter. After a while the astonishing new wheel ran as many as 120 spindles at once. Hargreaves had succeeded in making thread faster than ever before. But the spinning jenny could not make it tight and strong enough to be used as warp threads.

Still the spinners considered the machines a threat, and many jennies were smashed just as Kay's flying shuttle had been. But while the spinners were angry for one reason, the weavers complained for a different one. Since the jenny could not supply them with warp thread, they still had to wait for hand spinners to turn it out for them to use.

The impatient grumblings of the weavers were heard by Richard Arkwright, a young barber who traveled around buying hair to sell to wigmakers. Like many men of that time when spinning and weaving were done in most households, the barber knew something of both. Sparked by the weavers' complaints, a way of making strong thread began to shape in his clever mind. In 1771, Arkwright invented a better machine than Hargreaves' spinning jenny. He also built the first cotton mill in the world and ran his heavy spinning equipment by water- and horse-power. Two years later he built a mill for weaving calicoes on hand looms, for the power loom still had not been invented.

By 1775 Arkwright had taken out patents on the whole spinning process that, along with his spinning frame, for the first time made it possible to make cotton thread that was strong enough to use for warp.

Four years later, spinners stoned a mill of Awkwright's and smashed his machines wherever they could find them. Unlike Kay, though, and in spite of many threats and difficulties, the once poor barber was rewarded for his great contributions to the textile industry. A few years before he died, leaving a large fortune, he was knighted by the king.

Now the fast-growing cloth industry waited only for someone to combine the best features of Hargreaves' jenny and Arkwright's horse-power spinning frame. And that is exactly what was done by a man named Samuel Crompton.

Crompton's boyhood was a good deal like a mystery story. He lived in part of a creaky old mansion, known as Hall-in-the-Wood, where his mother forced him and a lame uncle to spin and weave. Often, as young Samuel spun thread on one of Hargreaves' spinning jennies, the cotton broke and Mrs. Crompton was very cross.

Probably it was because he wanted more time for the violin which he loved to play, and for mathematics, which he studied at night school, that Samuel determined to invent a way to make stronger thread.

When he was twenty-one the shy, handsome young man began to work in secret to improve spinning. He did not even let his mother or his uncle know what he was doing, and the strange sounds of his model-making caused the neighbors to be sure that ghostly old Hall-in-the-Wood was really haunted. Still Samuel kept on, paying for the material he needed by playing his violin in the village theater's orchestra.

As we already know, it is such men of vision, determination and knowledge of their subject who have made possible the miracle of the man-made fibers which are created for us in today's laboratories. Unhappily, not all of these tireless workers have had the success they deserve.

After five years of secret experiments Samuel finally did make a spinning frame he called a *mule*, which turned out strong, fine thread. At once there was a big demand for it. People longed to know how it was spun. One man went so far as to spy on Crompton through a hole he cut in the young man's ceiling. Others tried to bribe his workers to tell them the secret. Still others climbed up and stared in Samuel's windows. Finally the inventor of the spinning mule had to take his machine apart and hide it.

In spite of his gifted mind and his skill, Crompton was not a good businessman. He had no money to patent his invention, so he turned it over to some manufacturers he thought were honest. They never paid him a penny. When Crompton died he was almost as poor as John Kay, the inventor of the fly shuttle, had been. This seems all the more unfair when we know that it was the spinning mule which for the first time made it possible for English textile workers to make cotton cloth which rivaled that of India.

The mule was a good spinning machine. But it took skillful men to run it. The high wages they demanded made manufacturers look for a simpler one. A spinning machine that could be (and unfortunately was) operated by young children was invented in 1830, in England. Two years later, in America, another easily run thread-making machine was invented.

Meanwhile the once hungry looms were being supplied with more thread than could be woven. Half a century after Kay invented the fly shuttle a much better one was invented by Edmund Cartwright, a minister. At first Cartwright's loom was hard to run—a great deal harder than weaving by hand. But after several years he at last turned out a practical power loom and built a factory where he could manufacture his new machines. Again workers who were afraid machines would take their jobs from them tried to destroy the looms. They made a lot of trouble, but progress in spinning and weaving could no more be stopped in those times than it can be today. More spinning mills, more cloth factories, and faster and better looms went on appearing. By 1833, there were eighty-five thousand looms in England alone.

The little cotton plant whose story had begun so simply had helped to change the whole fabric-making picture in England, in Europe and in America. Cotton also built an empire in which it had no rival, as we shall see.

But cotton would never have become so powerful without the help of still another amazing invention—Eli Whitney's cotton engine, or cotton gin as he called it for short.

The early American colonists, you recall, had at first found cotton hard to grow and harvest. Gradually, though, quite large crops were raised in Georgia, North and South Carolina and other parts of the South. But even in the milder climates where the plant grew well and there were slaves to harvest it, there was a big problem. It took a man an entire day to clean one single pound. And all the time the improved spinning and weaving machines needed more cotton and every English ship that landed in America brought orders for it.

"Cotton could make us rich," said the growers, "if only it did not take so long to clean the seeds out of the fibers."

Those cotton-growers could not guess that a farm boy who was born on December 8, 1765, in Westboro, Massachusetts, would solve the problem for them and for the world.

Eli Whitney learned a great deal about machinery in his father's shop and when he was only thirteen he built the first machine for making nails. He worked his way through Yale and then became a tutor to some children on a Georgia plantation. It was there that, after she saw how well young Eli repaired the children's broken toys, the widow of General Nathanael Greene suggested that he make a machine for cleaning cotton.

"I have never even seen a cotton plant," Whitney objected. Next day, though, he looked at some cotton. The problem of how to clean it interested him at once. Without telling anyone, he began to try to make a device for cleaning the seeds out of the fluffy white fibers.

Eli Whitney finished his cotton gin in 1793, only a year after he began to work on it. The machine, which paved the way for the giant cotton industry, was praised by such great men as George Washington and Thomas Jefferson. And no wonder. For Whitney's gin could clean a thousand pounds of cotton in one day— a thousand times as much as a man could clean without it.

How did it work? Whitney used hooks to pull fibers through an opening that was too small for the seeds to go through—the same principle that is followed today.

With Whitney's wonder-working machine, cotton had led the way to another great advance in the textile field. The now famous cotton gin soon made the South the leading cotton region of the world. In eighteen years, United States cotton exports climbed from 487,-000 pounds to sixty-two million.

By 1860 more than half of the world's cotton was raised in the five states of the South which had become the little plant's kingdom. All through the first half of the nineteenth century, the great Mississippi River was King Cotton's royal highway. Along its banks night fires signaled to passing steamboats that the white treasure was there ready to be shipped to home ports and to the great capitals beyond our shores. During the day the planters' private landing places seethed with activity. And all the time the gold that cotton brought poured in.

Then came the Civil War and with it near-disaster. But once the bitter fight between North and South came to an end, courageous men began to rebuild and expand the cotton industry.

Today, though many nations produce it, the United States grows and uses more cotton than any other country. The little plant's empire has spread far beyond those five original states, too. Cotton is now raised in a huge region which extends from Virginia on the Atlantic Ocean to California on the Pacific, from the southeast corner of Missouri to the Gulf of Mexico.

And cotton has not stopped prodding men on to invent better machines and methods.

On huge plantations, four-row planters now plant and fertilize, in one operation, thirty to forty acres a day, and a tractor-mounted rotary hoe can cultivate sixty acres or even more in a day. Flame-throwers patterned after those of the war kill weeds and grass near the cotton stalk, while every day at certain seasons airplanes fly over hundreds of acres, dusting and spraying cotton crops to protect them from pests. When the crop is ready to be picked, the latest wonders of

the cotton patch, the mechanical pickers, can harvest as much as ten acres a day.

As we know, cotton is the most used of all fibers. It is also the only one we get from nature which is stronger when it is wet than when it is dry. Besides giving us cloth, this useful plant gives us drugs and plastics, thanks to modern science. Needless to say, cotton keeps a great many people busy. In our country alone, thirteen million people work in the vast cotton industry.

But cotton and flax are not the only vegetable fibers

for which man has found uses. Besides these two major ones there are a number of less important fibers that have served us faithfully and well. Hemp has long, strong, naturally waterproof fibers that are ideal for ships' ropes and sails. Jute, another long, easily spun fiber from India, is used here for gunny sacks. Ramie, a Chinese nettle, can be made into strong, silklike cloth. The light, fluffy fiber inside the seedpod of kapok is fine for mattresses, pillows and life preservers. And from the big, swordlike leaves of Yucatan's sisal plant, twine is made.

Truly the vegetable kingdom has been generous to man in his long search for textile material. And so has the animal kingdom, as you will see when you turn the page.

But what about the world of minerals?

A thousand years ago at least, cloth was woven from a fibrous structure found in certain rocks. This fabric is called asbestos and it is of great value because it is highly resistant to fire. It is used for theater curtains, different kinds of insulation and many other things.

6: THE WOOL STORY

"BAA, baa, black sheep, have you any wool?" asks the old, familiar rhyme. Then, as we all know, the little sheep answers: "Yes, sir, yes, sir, three bags full."

Today if that same question were asked of all the sheep in the entire world, the correct answer, for one year alone, would be: "Yes, sir, yes, sir, four thousand million pounds."

That is how huge the yearly wool crop has become. Of all the natural fibers, wool is the most used of any except cotton.

Raising sheep is a tremendous industry, and the beginnings of its long, adventurous history are lost in the mists of time. No one knows whether it was flax or wool that was first spun into thread. But because wool fibers are composed of microscopic scales which catch and cling, they are easy to spin together. So we may be certain that cloth made from them was one of the first fabrics that man ever used for clothing.

The first sheep we know anything about were in Central Asia. They were so valuable that their owners took their flocks along with them when they migrated across Africa and Europe. In this way, no doubt, wool production spread from place to place.

About A.D. 43, when the Romans invaded Britain, sheep had already been raised on the island for a long time. Perhaps to make it easier to keep their army well supplied with clothes, the Roman conquerors built a woolen factory and did a great deal to improve British spinning and weaving.

Long before this, however, woolen cloth had already achieved great beauty and value in other parts of the world. As far back as the days of the ancient lake villages, people had wanted fabric that was handsome as well as useful. So after the wool had been spun into drab, gray yarn, the women colored it with dyes they made from plants gathered in the great forests. One group, whom the Romans called Picti, or painted people, also dyed their bodies blue with a concoction they made by boiling woad, a plant root.

Centuries before the Christian era, while the Egyptians were weaving their robes of fresh, white linen, the people of Mesopotamia seem to have preferred robes made from the fleece of their famous sheep. Records, kept on clay tablets, show that these people of the region which is now Iraq had clothmaking shops in all of their big cities. Once a year, ships loaded with their fabrics and other goods were sent to foreign ports to be traded for the treasures of other lands. Textiles also traveled over the great trade routes to Egypt by caravan. Sometimes these trips were perilous adventures, for robbers and murderers often lay in wait to steal the valuable goods.

The Phoenicians, who lived along the narrow strip of Arabian coast which we know as Palestine, followed the somewhat earlier Minoans of Crete as the chief traders and sailors of ancient times. They traded their riches for raw Grecian and Syrian wool, which they dyed and wove and then shipped off again. Of the Phoenician trading posts that grew into big cities, Carthage, near where Tunis, North Africa, now stands, was the most powerful. The world's finest cloth was woven there and shipped to all the ports of the Mediterranean. Some believe that when the Romans made a rubble heap of Carthage they took home a number of the long-fleeced sheep they found there. Perhaps that Carthaginian breed is the ancestor of today's celebrated flocks, the Merinos.

Though cloth manufacture was to improve so fast later on, it seems to have stood still for a long time. For in the time of the early Greeks, wool was carded, spun and woven almost exactly as it had been several thousand years before in the lake villages. Like the lake villages, too, each Greek household made its own cloth. If more than enough was woven, it was traded for other things. In fact, cloth was a fine thing to have to exchange in those days because it could be carried easily without fear of damage; it did not spoil like food and it was needed by everyone. But sometimes it was sold for the iron bars which the early Greeks used as money.

Each of the gods of those early Greeks had at least one temple where he was worshiped at certain times of the year. During these seasons, skillful workers gathered in a small shop close to the temple and made gorgeous robes for their gods' statues. Sometimes cloth woven in the temple shops was sold to keep the temple repaired and to buy the priests' food. After a while it became customary to sell cloth made in the temple shops, and out of this grew the custom of making cloth in small shops instead of only at home.

Greek textile workers had clubs, or guilds—organizations of people engaged in the same craft. These Greek clubs had celebrations in honor of Minerva, the goddess of weavers. They also traded craft secrets at meetings. Guilds forced members to keep their work and the training of beginners up to standard.

The little workshops of early Greece grew into the factory-like ones of later times where workers went on strike, as they do now. The factories specialized, also. Some made sturdy wool for the capes of Greek soldiers. Others made only the finest white wool for the rich. In alleys back of the town's marble buildings were dye shops, cleaning shops, weaving shops and so on.

Towns as well as shops specialized, besides. It was not unusual for wool to be dyed in one town, then sent far away to another to be woven, then to still a third to be embroidered. But rich Greeks liked best to wear clothes made in the city of Athens, which set the styles of the country, much as today New York and Paris set our styles.

Finally the cloth of Greece began to travel to foreign ports. By the fifth century B.C., the Greeks had become the leading traders of the Mediterranean. But just as the Phoenicians and Minoans had had to bow to others, so, at last, did this proud island people. For after the Romans got control of all Italy, they claimed the sea, as well. They built amazing roads that made travel easier than it had ever been or would be again until the coming of the railroads hundreds and hundreds of years later. This made them masters of the trade routes, too.

As their marching armies spread the Roman Empire over the Mediterranean world, the Romans became more and more luxury-loving and richer and richer fabrics were taken home. At the same time in European towns that they controlled, clothmaking was doing a wonderful business. Wool and other textile fibers were carried over the well-policed roads from Spain and other far places. Many towns grew into huge weaving centers. One in what is now France is said to have had a population of over two hundred thousand.

But the mighty Empire, too, was doomed. It had reached out too far. The poor had to pay heavy taxes. Slaves brought from conquered places took over their jobs. Along the borders of the Empire were bitter enemies, and even some Romans turned against their government. By the year A.D. 476 Rome's power over the West had ended.

Now began a dark time for Europe. With no more Roman soldiers to guard the trade routes or even the roads from one town to another, travel and trade were impossible. People could not visit or communicate beyond the shortest distance. There was nothing to buy or to sell. With nothing to work with, skills were almost forgotten. Much knowledge was lost. A terrible blight fell on the world.

With Rome's fall, Europe broke up into tiny kingdoms where fortress castles became the only possible places of safety. Those who could not live within their shelter stayed nearby in huts. Once again the women of these little homes took over most of the work of carding, spinning and weaving. But in those bad times even the coarsest woolen or linen cloth was very hard to get, and the poor wore their clothes until they fell apart in rags.

But as the years passed, cloth fairs, like big open markets, began to be established where the war lords, at least, could buy fabrics. The ladies of the castles learned to weave and to make tapestries, and traveling weavers appeared, braving the dangers of those lawless times to go from house to house, making homemade yarns into patterned cloth that took more skill than the housewife had.

Other weavers had never left the ruins of what had been the great textile towns of Roman days. Gradually freemen moved to these towns, where they found a better life than they could have in the shadow of the castles whose lords treated them like slaves. Little by little the cloth centers grew more like those of the Greeks. They, too, had special shops for dyeing, spinning and so on. They, too, had guilds. The quality of cloth again improved until some of it was so valuable that wills were made telling just who should inherit it. Progress was, of course, made in other fields also, and once again invincible man emerged from the tunnel of ignorance and fear.

Until the thirteenth century, the Flemish (who lived in what is present-day Belgium and Holland) were the major manufacturers of woolen cloth in Europe. The English, on the other hand, were the major producers of raw wool. The Flemish bought raw wool from England, wove it into cloth and sent much of it back to be sold to the English.

Then the English decided to build up their own woolen cloth industry. They had tried to do this at various times since the Norman Conquest by encouraging skillful Flemish weavers to settle in England, but English cloth had never sold as well as the woolen products of the continent—even among the English, who liked the foreign fabrics better than the homemade cloth.

Now the English weavers formed guilds similar to those of the early Greeks. To help the native industry, English kings forbade the importation of foreign woolen cloth into England and the exportation of English raw wool to other countries. But by this time the

English raw wool, which was finer than any except the Spanish, was in great demand abroad, and so it was smuggled out. The smugglers were known as "owlers" because they worked at night.

Later, during the reign of Queen Elizabeth I, raw wool was for a time freely exported, and during this period woolen manufacturing—and the country as a whole—prospered greatly. The wool trade was of so much benefit to England that from about that period on it has been the custom for the Lord Chancellor, when presiding over the House of Lords, to sit on a seat stuffed with wool—called the Woolsack—as a reminder of the importance of wool in the nation's economy.

About half a century after Elizabeth died, however, stern laws were again passed to keep Britain's "golden fleece" at home. Even though they did no good at all —and, in fact, hurt the wool trade—they stayed in force for 165 years, until long after the amazing spinning and weaving machines had been invented and had put cotton, instead of wool, in first place.

Among the many strange, restrictive laws which the English passed during the course of this long struggle was one which compelled students, professors and judges to wear gowns of English wool, and another which required that the dead must be buried in woolen shrouds!

But when all these measures failed to put the English woolen industry on its feet, foreign workers were again brought in to teach the English how to make better cloth. That was the turning-point. From that time on, wool has been the "growing gold" of Britain.

Since wool has been so important to mankind through the ages, it was natural that when the early colonists came to America they brought a small flock of sheep with them. We have already read how well these sheep were cared for and how they increased— so much so that thirty-five years after the colonists crossed the ocean they had a thousand of the animals.

Even that number of sheep, however, could not supply enough wool for the industrious American settlers, who would have been glad to buy it in England. But English clothmakers wanted the colonists to buy their cloth, rather than raw wool to weave. They got a law passed which forbade sending wool, woolen yarn or even sheep out of England. Still the Americans refused to be forced into buying English cloth. Instead, they bought raw wool from Spain and from Holland. They raised more sheep, too, and made their wool go farther by combining it with flax in the linsey-woolsey material we already know about.

By 1675, they had enough wool to send to France, Spain and Portugal in exchange for products of those countries. The colonists' brisk trade angered the British so much that in 1699 they ruled that the Americans must not move their own wool or linen even from one colony to another. They forbade the colonists to load any ship with it. They went so far as to threaten to cut off the right hands of colonists who tried to improve their flocks of sheep.

But American clothmaking went right on. By the time of our first Independence Day, seventy-seven years after the British tried to kill the growing American textile industry, the colonists had wool—and flax, too—in plenty, and all of their wool was grown, carded, spun and woven right on America's own soil.

Today the woolen goods we use are not by any means all produced here in America. The sheep population of the world is six hundred million, and vast flocks graze over huge areas of South Africa, South America, Australia, New Zealand and, of course, our own western states, while smaller flocks can be found in many other places.

In most regions, live sheep are sheared by traveling groups of workers who can shear up to two hundred a day with the power clippers they use. Shearing is done once a year; the fleece comes off almost whole, then is baled to go to market. Of course, shearing does not hurt sheep any more than it hurts a person to have his hair cut.

From the ranches or farms where the shearing is done, the wool is shipped to central markets. From these it goes to the mills, which buy the special type and quality of wool they need for the fabric they manufacture.

When the fleece reaches the mills, it is spread on tables topped with wire mesh, where the different kinds of fibers are sorted. The fleece of one sheep alone has many different types of fibers. The sides and shoulders, for example, grow the long, fine wool which is used in worsted materials. Shorter fibers and lamb's wool are used in woolen materials.

Right now, though, we had better find out what is meant by the two words *woolen* and *worsted*. Since both fabrics are made of wool, can there be much difference?

Yes, there is. For woolens are made from yarns of the shorter fibers and sometimes from blends with other fibers. Such things as jerseys, tweeds, sweaters, blankets and flannels are made of woolen material. Usually they are rather fuzzy in appearance and soft to the touch.

Worsted fabric, on the other hand, is made from yarn spun from fibers that have been selected for their length and fineness. Such yarn is smooth-surfaced. Fabric made of it is more or less smooth, too, depending on the way it is finished. Gabardine suits and coats and serge materials are typical worsteds. They resist dirt well, do not wrinkle easily, and are very long-wearing.

But whether it is to go into soft woolens or harder-surfaced worsteds, after wool has been sorted it must be *scoured*. This is done by a series of baths which remove the animal grease and other matter sticking to the fleece.

Next the fibers are carded. Instead of using a crude card like Neo's, mills nowadays use big, revolving drums covered with stiff, toothlike wires, which remove trash and separate the fibers that cling together in a kind of web. The carding method varies depending on whether the desired result is to be worsted or woolen yarns. While the carding is going on, the short fibers are being removed. If this is a mill for making worsted, they will be sent to a woolen mill to be spun. But the long fibers intended for worsteds must again be combed and then wound into a huge ball, called a *top,* which may weigh as much as fifteen pounds. After these tops have been spun, the yarn is wound onto warp drums which often contain enough yarn to make ten thousand yards of fabric. Thread from these drums becomes the warp or up-and-down threads on big power-driven looms. On modern looms the shuttle carrying the weft, or crosswise, thread flies back and forth so fast that one cannot see it.

After either woolens or worsteds are woven, they go through a very important step called *fulling.* During this step the newly woven cloth (which is still rather loosely held together) is passed between revolving rollers under pressure, in vats filled with warm, soapy water. As the fibers interlock, the fabric is shrunk and compressed. This process makes it strong and durable.

Next, if the fabric is a woolen, it is brushed with a kind of vegetable burr, called a *teazel,* which has been used for generations. These burrs brush up an uneven nap which is then sheared off with a machine rather like a tiny lawn mower.

If the fabric is worsted, it is not brushed. It is sheared very close, after which it is steamed and pressed.

At some point during its trip from the sheep's back to the store where it is to be sold, wool is dyed. Sometimes it does not go into the dye vats until it is in the form of woven cloth. But wool, which dyes readily, can be dyed in the fleece or after it has been wound into tops. It can be dyed even after it has been spun into yarn.

As you can see, even with up-to-date methods and machinery, wool must go through quite a number of steps before it becomes a coat, a dress, a blanket, a rug or any one of the many useful things which are made of it. It has so many splendid qualities, however, that we can easily understand why this natural, animal fiber has proved invaluable to mankind throughout its age-old history.

Not only can wool fabric be very beautiful; it is also warm, rugged and long-wearing. Its natural springiness helps it to "shed" wrinkles. It does not catch fire easily. It is absorbent and comfortable in different temperatures, to mention only a few of its many virtues.

In spite of all these good points, though, wool, like other fibers, has some drawbacks. As we know, it comes from the sheeplands full of burrs, dirt and trash, and must go through a complicated process before it is made into cloth. Wool also has a tendency to shrink when put into hot water, so it cannot be washed with the rest of the laundry. Extra care must be taken in pressing it and in keeping it mothproof.

Science is already overcoming some of these faults, and we can be sure that wool will one day add new triumphs to its long record of faithful service to man, in whose progress it has played a major part.

Now, however, let us hear the story of the other leading fiber which is supplied to us by an animal—this one not by a good-sized sheep, but by a very tiny insect.

7: SILK: CHINA'S FABULOUS TREASURE

As WE learn more about the stories of the four major natural textile fibers, it appears that each of them has had its hour of triumph and then has had one of the other three take its place, at least for a while, as man's favorite.

Certainly that is true of silk. For, as the luxury queen of fabrics, the fantastic product of the tiny silkworm enjoyed a long, romantic reign.

Smugglers, kidnapers, bandits, gold and jewels all have their place in the story of the wonder which is silk. And we must remember, too, that along with spices, it was silk that helped to lure Columbus to this part of the world in the mistaken belief that he was blazing a new trail to the riches of the East.

Although it is a true one, the story of silk may well begin like a fairy tale.

Once upon a time in the China of forty-five hundred years ago, we are told, the Empress Si-ling was the first person to discover that silk could be made into fabric. She wove its shining threads into a gorgeous robe for her husband, the Emperor. Afterward she taught the poor people of her country the secret of silk so that they, too, could become prosperous. As a reward for her goodness to them, the Chinese named Si-ling the goddess of silk. Until modern times it was the custom for the reigning empress to dress in her finest silken clothes and carry gifts to Si-ling's temple each spring.

China's climate did not preserve for us the magnificent robes, temple hangings and other silken treasures which the Chinese learned to make in those early days. Nor have we pictures like those in Egypt's tombs, to tell us about them. But the Chinese have been civilized so long that we do have written records that date back several thousand years.

From these old writings we know, among other things, that the people of China bribed their savage Tartar neighbors with their wonderful silk. It is said that they sometimes turned over as many as half a million pieces of silk in a single year to keep the Tartars from raiding and destroying Chinese towns.

As the centuries passed, silk traveled farther and farther over the trade routes to other countries and made China very rich. But all this time the Chinese kept the source of their treasure a secret, and the foreigners who traded their gold for it grew more and more desperate to solve the mystery of how silk was made. Chinese law, however, doomed to death anyone who even tried to take out of the country either silkworms or the seed from which grew the mulberry trees on which they fed.

When, about 330 B.C., Alexander the Great swept through Asia into India, he found silk there and took it to Europe. Seeing the glistening wonder for the first time, people marveled at it. What did it come from? It was hundreds of years before the answer was known.

When you have seen a shining length of silk or a lovely, shimmering silk dress whose delicate folds catch the light almost as a jewel does, perhaps you, too, have wondered about it.

How can a small insect, and a worm at that, create a substance that can become beautiful silk fabric?

The secret has been known for a long time now. How it is thought to have finally escaped from China we shall hear later. Before we do, though, let's get a close-up view of a silkworm and find out about the process that, if we had lived centuries ago, we might have given anything we owned to discover. As you will soon learn, this process is vital to the development of today's miraculous, man-made fibers. So we shall follow it step by step.

At present the finest natural silk comes from silkworms carefully raised on "farms." In their final stage as moths, the insects lay their tiny eggs on cloths or sheets of paper on which the silk farmer has put them. (The eggs stick to these sheets just as, when silkworms were in their wild state, the eggs stuck to leaves.) The farmer then places the sheets of eggs in a cool place for six months of a kind of sleep, called *hibernation*. At the end of this period, the pinhead-size eggs are set in a warmer spot for developing and hatching. The newly hatched baby worms, known as *larvae,* are next put on feeding trays where they greedily eat the finely chopped, young, green leaves from white mulberry trees. On this diet the infant worms grow so fast that they outgrow their skins and shed them three or four times. In five or six weeks the silkworms are three

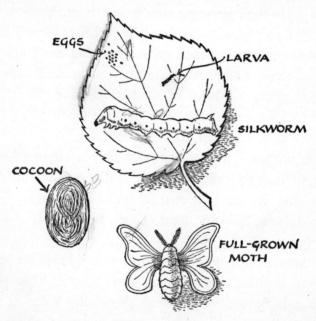

EGGS

LARVA

SILKWORM

COCOON

FULL-GROWN
MOTH

inches long and are fully grown. At this stage each worm eats twenty times its weight in food. In fact, between the time they hatch and the time they spin their cocoons, the silkworms from a single ounce of eggs may eat more than a ton of mulberry leaves. But the farmers know they are well worth all this food. For that ounce of eggs gives him worms enough to produce twelve pounds of raw silk.

When, at last, the silkworms stop eating and begin a kind of rearing-up motion, that is the signal that they are ready to spin their cocoons. Workers put them on trays covered with small twigs or something on which they will start to spin.

The small silkworms now fasten lines to the twigs and begin their spinning with a fine thread that comes out of a pair of minute tubes in their lower jaws. These tiny openings are called *spinnerets*. You are going to come across that word quite often as you hear about the wonderful fabrics of modern science. The silkworm's spinnerets were to be the clue leading to a discovery that has changed our world.

Silkworms spun for centuries before anyone knew exactly how they made the thread that could be turned into silk, the most coveted fabric of kings and nobles of old. Now, however, we do know. Briefly, this is what happens:

The silkworm has glands on each side of its body which manufacture a gummy substance. This substance is pushed out through those tiny holes in the jaws, called spinnerets, which we just read about. A very fine strand comes out of each of the two holes; then the two separate strands join together in one long, continuous one. This threadlike strand, or filament, hardens the instant it comes in contact with the air.

The first thing silkworms do is wrap themselves in an outer network of these filaments (rather like putting on a coat that is too big for you). Then they spin inward until their bodies are completely enclosed. After about seventy-two hours of spinning, the cocoons are finished. Sound asleep inside of them, the silkworms change into full-grown moths.

After about two weeks in their cocoons, the moths would be ready to come out into the world for the few hours that is their entire life span. But in breaking through the cocoon, they would cut the one long, valuable thread of which it is made, into numbers of useless, short ones. For this reason only those moths which are to be kept for laying eggs will be allowed to hatch.

The cocoons which are to be used for silk are steamed to kill the moths inside and keep them from hatching. Next they are sorted and soaked to soften their natural gum. Finally they are unwound. Amazingly, each cocoon may unwind to a length of more than half a mile of unbroken silk strand.

Such surprisingly long, fine strands must have been a wonderful find for Empress Si-ling who, we are told, was their discoverer over four thousand years ago. According to the story, she saw silkworms drawing their shining threads across a leaf or twig and, believing that she could make lovely material from them, she began to raise the insects for that purpose.

Whether or not this was the actual beginning of China's rich silk industry, we cannot be sure. But it is a fact that the Chinese have known how to cultivate and weave silk for almost five thousand years. We know, too, that they kept their art from the rest of the world for all of two thousand years and got huge prices for the silk thread and fabric they sold.

But the secret of silk was too valuable to stay forever in China, even though the penalty for telling it was death.

In about the third century, some Japanese managed to kidnap a number of young Chinese girls from the silk-weaving village where they lived. They took them home and forced them to teach their art to the people of Japan.

A little later India learned how to make silk in an even more daring way, all because a Chinese princess was engaged to marry an Indian prince.

Before the princess left her home for the long journey to the prince's country, where the wedding was to be, the prince sent one of his trusted servants to her with a message of great importance.

We can picture the black-haired, almond-eyed princess in the beautiful palace garden where surely there were some willow trees and a little bridge over a brook. Probably she moved a short distance away from her maids so that she might be alone to hear what the prince's messenger had to tell her.

"His Highness sends me to say that there is no silk in our country," the servant whispered. "No precious silk in all the great land of India."

The princess looked astonished. What a strange message to send all this way to me, she thought. Then she understood. When she went to meet the prince in his own country, he wished her to bring with her the mysterious means of making silk, whatever it might be. For none outside of China knew for certain how the glorious silk fabrics were made, and many believed the thread for weaving them came from a flower.

The Chinese princess, of course, knew the truth. For hundreds of years it had been the custom for the ladies of the royal household to care for silkworms and to make the silk from their cocoons into splendid robes which the emperor wore each year when he made offerings to the spirits of the earth and the sky.

But it was forbidden that anyone should take the secret out of China. The princess trembled at the thought of what the prince asked of her. If she were caught she would have to die. Yet how could she refuse the request of the man she was to marry?

She gave the prince's messenger a frightened sign and returned to her maids, pretending the man had only brought her instructions for her journey. Then for many hours at night she lay awake, planning how she would accomplish her dangerous mission. In the daytime she made cautious preparations.

When she left the palace for the last time, accompanied by her maids, she wore an unusually elaborate and large headdress. Hidden away in its lining were silkworm eggs and many seeds of the white mulberry trees, which would have to be planted in India for the silkworms to feed upon.

We are told that the princess passed China's frontier in safety and that in this way the cultivation of silk began in India.

Silk came to what is now Istanbul in a strange way, too. There, in about A.D. 550, two Persian monks who had once lived in China and also knew the answer to the riddle of silk were persuaded to go back to China and smuggle silkworm eggs out in a hollow bamboo cane. It is a fact of history that from the contents of that cane were descended all the silkworms that supplied the Western world for over twelve hundred years.

Though for such long ages it had lived only in China, the silkworm was perfectly at home in many of the new countries to which it gradually spread. Italy, however, was for five hundred years the leading silk-producing nation and, along with China and Japan, remains to this day one of the three foremost silk producers of the world.

Because beautiful silk was the favorite of kings, queens, and wealthy and fashionable persons everywhere, almost everyone wanted it. (As we know, it was even cultivated in the United States for a time, and Pennsylvania had a silk industry in which Benjamin Franklin was interested.) But silkworms are often victims of disease, and raising them and making silk has always been a long, painstaking and costly business. Many women have lived all their lives without ever owning a silk dress, while countless others who could boast such a luxury saved it for great occasions, knowing it must last for years.

Today, although fine-quality natural silk is still expensive, it is popular and no doubt the little silkworm will never be out of a job. Yet in our modern world silk has a number of serious rivals. And oddly enough, it was the silkworm itself that finally showed man how to create the fibers which would one day be as beautiful as silk, would cost much less and would have some desirable qualities that silk lacks.

In the next chapter we will find out how China's secret treasure finally started science on the search for the miracle fabrics we now have.

8: THE SEARCH FOR THE PERFECT FIBER

Now that we have read something of the histories of the natural fibers, we know that all of them have certain drawbacks. Some are subject to disease and blight. Some require huge amounts of hand labor which machines have not yet been able to replace. Some can be produced only in certain climates.

Through the ages man has put his intelligence to work to make life more comfortable, so it is not surprising that he grew impatient of the limitations of the textile fibers he found in nature. He began at last to dream that he might make a fiber himself that would always be plentiful as well as beautiful and that would be reasonable in price. Just when this dream began we do not know.

We do know, however, that although the perfect fiber has not been invented even yet, the search for it has been going on for a long time. And the idea of man-made textiles has fascinated people for generations.

Rayon, the first successful man-made fiber, has been continuously manufactured in the United States only since 1911. But as an idea it has existed in the minds of men since Isaac Newton's time.

The first hint we have that anything like rayon was being thought of is in the writings of Robert Hooke, a seventeenth-century Englishman who was famous for his work with an optical instrument that was brand-new in his day—the microscope. In 1667, after examining some natural silk under his microscope, Hooke wrote of the possibility of finding a way to make artificial silk that might be even better than the real thing.

It was ninety years, though, before anyone else that we know of started thinking along the same startling lines. Then Reaumur, a French naturalist and physicist, wrote a book called *History of Insects*. In it he stated: "Silk is only a liquid gum which has been dried. Could we not make silk ourselves with gums and resins?" He pointed out that it had been proven possible to make varnishes that had the basic qualities of silk and on which solvents, water and ordinary heat had no effect. If he had threads of varnish, he thought he could make them into fabrics as strong and brilliant as silk.

"It does not seem impossible," said Reaumur, "to spin threads as fine as natural silk when we consider to what an extent art may be carried."

The "art" that Reaumur meant was demonstrated in his own day by Bon, another French naturalist, who succeeded in making a delicate yarn by twisting together fine spider filaments. This yarn was actually knit into a pair of stockings. But though such patient work was a great curiosity, it had no value except to spur on the hunt for a man-made fiber.

Reaumur never saw fibers made of varnish, and another hundred years were to pass before a man-made fiber was finally created. Several developments, all made by trained scientists, paved the way for the dramatic event.

In 1855 a Swiss chemist, George Audemars, changed cellulose (a substance found in all living plants) from a solid into a gummy, half-liquid solution and got a patent on a way to make it into fine threads. His method imitated the silkworm's. For when the silkworm eats mulberry leaves it is eating cellulose, which it then turns into the thick liquid out of which it spins its cocoon.

Though Audemars' way of making threads failed, the idea of changing a solid into a semiliquid, and then back again into a solid in another form, is still the major principle in the manufacture of all types of rayon.

No one realized it at the time, but another step in the search was taken in 1870 when John Hyatt, an American inventor, developed *pyroxylin,* a cellulose treated with nitric acid, which is the material used in making celluloid.

Still, up to this time nobody had thought of a really good way to make long or fine threads of any of these man-made substances. Audemars had tried putting a needle into his cellulose solution and had drawn it out into threads the way you test candy or cake frosting with a spoon to see when it is cooked enough. But the threads were thicker at one end than at the other, and made in this way, different threads were of different thicknesses, too. So Audemars' attempt failed and nothing of importance in the mechanical line was invented for making man-made fibers for almost twenty more years.

Who could have guessed that the amazing invention of the electric light bulb would take science a stride nearer to solving the mystery of how to make fibers? But that is what happened. For in 1883 in England where the search began, Sir Joseph Swan made an instrument for forcing liquid cellulose through fine holes in a metal plate, in order to create an inexpensive filament for an electric light bulb he devised some time before Edison's. In making long, unbroken filaments in this way, Swan, a physicist, had copied the silkworm's method and had invented the first spinneret—the very first of the thousands of threadmaking spinnerets that are used today in every man-made-fiber factory in the world.

Swan knew he had found a way to make a textile fiber as well as a light-bulb filament. But artificial silk made by his formula cost more than the real silk it imitated. So science seemed still to be a long way from its goal, and the search went on.

In the meantime, back in 1865, the great and famous Louis Pasteur had begun to work on a disease of silkworms which threatened to wipe out the important silk industry that supported so many French workers. Studying with him at the time was Count Hilaire de Chardonnet. While Pasteur found the cause of silkworm diseases and discovered how to prevent them, his pupil, inspired by the silkworm's own method, saw the possibility of making an artificial filament that would free his countrymen from their dependence on the delicate caterpillar that makes silk.

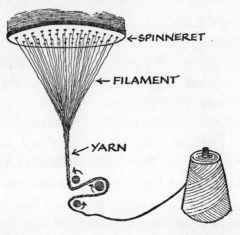

Later the Count was also attracted by the beautiful sheen and luster of the dried nitrocellulose that Hyatt invented. "How," he wondered, "could such a substance be used to make fibers, thread and, finally, woven cloth?"

But Chardonnet did a lot more than wonder about it. First of all, because the silkworm uses mulberry leaves as the source of its silk filament, Chardonnet used the mulberry tree itself as the source of his cellulose. He then turned the cellulose into nitrocellulose and next into liquid pyroxylin. In 1884, almost twenty years after he had started on his daring experiment, he succeeded in squirting a fine spray of pyroxylin through a spinneret in a special way and with a very important result. For he arranged it so that his spinneret sprayed the pyroxylin into a stream of warm air which rapidly evaporated the liquid solvents. This left solid, lustrous filaments ready to be wound on reels and eventually spun into thread for weaving.

Five years later, the Count's wife had a dress made of this amazing new man-made fiber to wear to the Paris Exposition. Hilaire de Chardonnet had succeeded where all the others had failed. To him must go the credit for developing the very first practical man-made fiber the world has ever known. But Chardonnet's triumph was not sudden. It came only after twenty-nine years of patient, intelligent, scientific work.

The artificial silk fabric he exhibited in Paris caused so much interest in this sensational new marvel that a factory for making it was built in 1891 in Chardonnet's home town, Besançon, in northern France. This plant ran successfully until the First World War, when the French government took it over for the manufacture of gun cotton.

A man-made fiber, the fabulous, long-dreamed-of goal of scientists, was a reality. However, in spite of Chardonnet's fine contribution, three other cellulose products and methods have replaced his fiber (which is no longer made commercially), and have become far more successful.

These are the three, from the least to the most important in quantities made and used: The *cuprammonium* process gives us what is known as Bemberg rayon.

The *cellulose acetate* process produces acetate rayon. The third is the *viscose* process which gives us much more than half of all the rayon used—viscose rayon. Because of its importance, the viscose process will be described in the next chapter. Meantime, we shall hear very briefly about the first two.

In the cuprammonium process, cellulose is dissolved in ammoniacal copper oxide, and though the chemical steps differ from the other processes, the mechanical steps of manufacture are about the same. The rayon produced by this method is still known by its German manufacturer's name, Bemberg.

Cellulose acetate is the chemical name of acetate rayon, the second in importance in the rayon family and discovered before either of the other two. But though it was known, it was used only as the coating material for the wings of airplanes when flying was a new art and wings were made of wood covered with cloth. Aviators and manufacturers of the day called the cloth coating "dope." At the end of the First World War, when the building of fighting planes stopped, a large English factory had to find a new use for the cellulose acetate "dope" they made there, or go out of business. Today's important acetate rayon process was the result.

In this process, purified cellulose is treated with acetic acid and acetic anhydride. When water is added to this mixture, cellulose acetate precipitates, which means that a solid drops out of solution and settles to the bottom of the vessel or container in which it is made. When it is to be used for making rayon fibers, this solid cellulose acetate is again dissolved. But this time the solvent is usually acetone, which you may know as the solvent in fingernail-polish remover.

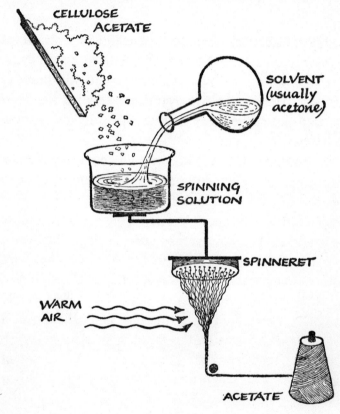

This solution is pumped through the spinneret into a draft of warm air. The air evaporates the acetone very rapidly, leaving the cellulose acetate solid again, in the form of filaments, ready for reeling, spinning and all the later processes leading to the final product.

The low cost of fibers produced by all three methods, along with their good looks and the comparative ease with which they could be spun, dyed and woven caused the rayon industry to grow at a surprising rate.

The world will always be grateful to Chardonnet for giving it an exciting new textile fiber. But, as we shall see later, he also presented textile men with a whole set of new problems. And though he lived until 1924, when the industry was already huge and still growing fast, the Count probably never dreamed what the fruits of his twenty-nine years of research and labor would be.

He predicted that his fiber would some day become many times more beautiful and useful than it was in its early form. But it is doubtful that he could ever have imagined the care, precision and ingenuity of the modern methods of manufacture which bring that beauty and usefulness into being.

9: RAYON: THE LABORATORY'S FIRST GIFT TO THE LOOM

You have just read how the French scientist Hilaire de Chardonnet finally found a way to make the "artificial silk" that was actually the grandfather of our modern rayon.

During the years since then, man-made textile fibers have come a very long way. They have climbed to such a high place that rayon is used more than any other textile fiber except cotton. But like almost all great advances, this one did not happen without a real struggle.

In its early days, the new fiber showed little sign that it would some day be so popular and useful. It began to be manufactured in the United States in 1911. But at first the fabric made from it was not good-looking or good-wearing. People gave it a cold welcome. As late as the 1920's, articles made of it often wound up on some bargain counter.

Men of vision, however, went on believing in the enormous possibilities of a fiber which man could create to suit his needs. In our own country, costly factories and research laboratories were built. Specially trained scientists worked tirelessly to improve the fiber. Experiments failed. Experiments succeeded. More careful work was done. More money was spent.

Before many years the quality and appearance of the fiber that imitated silk was greatly improved. It began to cost less to buy, and in 1924 it was even given a new, pleasant-sounding name—"rayon."

But rayon fiber did not keep on being something to use only in place of silk. With new developments came countless new uses. It can now be made into beautiful fabrics for many different kinds of clothes, draperies and so on. And manufacturers have learned to make the fiber so amazingly strong that it is widely used for tough, heavy-duty fabrics such as tire cord for trucks, jeeps and bombers; for safety belts, and for many other things of that kind. It also goes into handsome rugs and upholstery. In fact, every day this senior member of the man-made-fibers family adds to our comfort and well-being in many ways.

In spite of the many changes and improvements, the basic process for manufacturing rayon fiber is the same today as when it was first discovered. The process which is the most generally used, by far, is the viscose process. It can be divided into three big steps with a number of smaller ones in between.

Here are the three big, basic steps:

1. Cellulose, a solid substance which we get from trees and plants, must first be changed into a liquid.

2. The liquid is drawn out in fine, hairlike streams.

3. These liquid streams are changed into long, con-

tinuous, solid filaments, or threads, which are made into *continuous-filament yarn* or else cut into short lengths, called *staple,* for spinning into yarns in the same way as cotton yarn is made.

Solid to liquid and then back again to solid—this may sound like a strange way to make anything. But let's take a closer look and see just what happens in this extremely technical process.

First of all, what is this substance called *cellulose* which nature so obligingly supplies to our huge chemical industry?

The solid part of the cell walls of every blade of grass, every flower, bush and tree, is cellulose. But science has found that the cellulose which is best for making rayon comes from spruce, pine and hemlock trees, and from the short fibers called cotton linters which cling to cotton seeds after they have been separated from the cotton.

So to prepare for making rayon fiber the big trees must be cut down and the cotton linters collected. Afterward the trees are cut into logs, then chopped into small chips by machines. Next, both the wood chips and the cotton linters are cooked until they are pulp.

This, though, is no ordinary kind of cooking. It is done with live steam and with chemicals. This first part of the scientific process of making rayon usually takes place near the cotton fields and the forests where the plants and trees are grown.

Next, the pulpy mass is drained on sievelike, moving

screens. Then it is run through heavy rollers which squeeze out still more water and press the pulp into sheets. These sheets of cellulose are about the thickness of blotting paper and about the size of a newspaper page. In this form, the cellulose is shipped to the factory where the rayon fibers are to be made.

Once at the factory, the different lots of sheets are mixed together so that they will make a product of equal strength and quality. After this is done, the sheets are placed in presses where they are soaked in a chemical solution called sodium hydroxide, or caustic soda. This is a strong alkali, or acid neutralizer, and it eats away certain impurities. It also changes the cellulose sheets chemically into *alkali cellulose*. Remember that word *alkali*. For as you will see, it is very important to our chemical process.

When the sheets have had their carefully timed chemical bath, a hydraulic press is used to take out some, but not all, of the liquid from them. The amount that stays in is measured with great care so as to cause exactly the right chemical reaction.

Now the soft, moist sheets of alkali cellulose are taken from the presses and are fed into a "crumbing machine." This machine is known by the tongue-twisting name of *pfleiderer*. It has fast-turning blades which tear and break the sheets into fluffy bits called *alkali cellulose crumbs*.

Because the crumbs are still damp from their caustic-soda bath, the chemical action is still going on. This action is known as *aging*. It, too, is carefully timed, and a sharp watch is kept on the temperature of the crumbs, also.

At the end of this scientifically measured aging period, the crumbs are moved to big churns, somewhat like cement mixers. A strong-smelling chemical called liquid carbon disulphide is added. By the time this has been done, the crumbs are of such a chemical nature that they can easily be dissolved. That powerful wizard, chemistry, has also changed their color. They are now bright orange!

The crumbs' new chemical form goes by the name of *cellulose xanthate*. You pronounce that *x* the same way you do the one in xylophone, the musical instrument.

By now many things have happened to our cellulose since it left its native field and forest. Yet even with its new name, new orange color and new form, it has a little more to do before it takes the first of the three big steps on the way to becoming rayon fiber.

When the cellulose xanthate is taken out of the big churns, it is put into still another mixing machine. This one has revolving blades somewhat like a large egg beater. Some of that same caustic soda that we met at the very beginning of our chemical operation, and a lot of water, are added. Then the blades begin to whir.

When the machine is finally shut off there is not one particle of solid material left in it. The number-one step has been taken and it is a chemical triumph. Solid has become liquid. The cellulose xanthate crumb has been dissolved into a gluey, golden liquid which looks a good deal like honey.

Now the cellulose we have watched through all these chemical adventures must be renamed again. In its new liquid form it is *viscose solution*. The word viscose comes from the dictionary word *viscous,* which means gluelike, or sticky.

To make sure that the solution is just sticky enough, a steel ball is dropped into it. As the ball falls a certain distance, more careful timing is done. The length of time it takes the ball to fall shows how viscous, or gluey, the solution is.

At this point in the production of rayon, the way it will look when it is finished is decided on. If nothing at all is added to the clear viscose solution it will become a bright, shiny rayon when it is finished. But for many uses, dull or semidull rayon is more popular. So certain chemicals which are dulling agents are added. Add a lot of the dulling chemicals and the result will be rayon with no sheen at all; add a little and the result will be medium-dull rayon. Whichever amount is added—or if the dulling agent is left out altogether—the effect lasts as long as the fabric. Once added to the viscose solution the chemicals become part of the rayon itself. They cannot be washed or rubbed off like a coating.

Now that its future appearance is settled, the viscose solution goes into large tanks for still more aging. Its temperature is again controlled, and a vacuum device on each tank takes the bubbles out of the honey-like

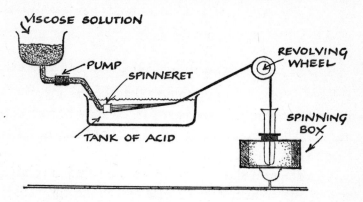

VISCOSE SOLUTION

PUMP

SPINNERET

REVOLVING WHEEL

SPINNING BOX

TANK OF ACID

fluid. Why? Because bubbles could cause breaks later on when the chemical "spinning" is done.

This "spinning" is the very next step—the second of the three big basic ones in the remarkable process of making rayon fibers. But we must remember that this type of spinning is entirely different from that used for spinning short natural fibers such as wool, cotton and flax into yarn.

As you read in Chapter 8, this chemical spinning is modeled on the way a silkworm spins its cocoon. Remember how the silkworm feeds on mulberry leaves and how, as it digests this food, a gluey substance forms in its glands? This liquid is then pressed out through two openings, called spinnerets, located below the worm's mouth. As the liquid comes out of the spinnerets and into contact with the air, the two shiny streams join and harden into one unbroken, hairlike filament.

If you will look at the accompanying diagram you will see how rayon viscose solution is forced by means

of a pump through a man-made spinneret so
that it, too, comes out of very small holes in fine
streams.

A modern spinneret is about the size of a thimble.
It is made of costly platinum so that the drilling of the
minute holes in this very hard metal may be very ac-
curate. These holes are so small they are almost invisible to the naked eye.

The diagram shows you the viscose solution coming
out of the spinneret in its new threadlike form. Step
two in the manufacture of rayon fiber has been taken:
liquid viscose has been drawn out in fine streams.

But those streams are still liquid. They are not yet
actual fibers.

Earlier in this chapter you were asked to remember
the word *alkali*. All through its many changes the
substance we have been watching has been made to
keep its non-acid characteristic. It has stayed alkaline.
As they come out of the spinneret the liquid streams
are still alkaline.

Now you will learn why they were kept that way.

Look again at the diagram. The tank contains
acid. As the alkaline-liquid streams enter the tank, the
chemical action of the acid bath is to turn them into
solid filaments. Liquid has become solid again in the
final one of the big basic steps of the magic-like process
of making rayon fiber.

One tiny fiber, as we know, is formed by each almost
invisible hole in the spinneret. But there are a great

many holes. Now, as the separate fibers are formed, all of those from one spinneret are pulled out of the tank of acid by a revolving wheel. Next they are drawn down into a rapidly whirling spinning box. The spinning box twists the many tiny filaments into a single rayon yarn, or thread, strong enough to be made into cloth.

It is strange to find that, after the many changes it has gone through since it left the cotton field and the forest, the cellulose which is the raw material from which rayon is made, is now back in its pure state. Instead of being cellulose in pulp form, however, it is cellulose in the form of yarn. Because it begins and ends in this way, rayon is often called "regenerated," or restored, cellulose. And because it is dependent on a substance which we get from nature, rayon is not a synthetic fiber like those we are going to read about very soon.

But let's go back to the brand-new yarn we left in the spinning box a minute ago.

As the box whirls around, it winds the rayon yarn into a hollow, cylinder-shaped form. This is called a *cake*. When enough yarn has been chemically spun into the spinning box, it is stopped and the cake is taken out.

In factories where rayon yarn is made, a great many such cakes are, of course, produced at the same time. When they leave the spinning boxes they are washed many times with soft, filtered water under a series of "showers." These and other treatments take away every trace of the acid bath and make the yarn thoroughly clean.

Next the clean cakes are placed on continuously moving carriers which take them slowly through automatic tunnel dryers. There they are dried and conditioned till they hold just the proper amount of moisture.

From the drying tunnels the cakes are put on various kinds of machines. These wind them into bobbins, skeins and other forms wanted by the different textile manufacturers who will weave or knit the yarn into finished fabrics.

What will those fabrics be? An important thing about this continuous-filament type of rayon yarn is its great strength. So a great deal of it will be used for the sturdy articles we read about earlier. But the same high strength properties also make it very good for spinning into extra-fine yarns for delicate fabrics.

But though we have seen our man-made miracle yarns off to the weaving and knitting mills to be made into many useful and beautiful things, this is not the end of the rayon story.

We have learned how smooth, unbroken strands of rayon are produced. But remember our third big step, in which we learned that the solid filaments or hair-fine strands could also be cut into short lengths, called *staple*.

One of the astonishing things about this rayon staple is that though it is a man-made fiber like the continuous filament rayon, it is not made into yarn in the same way at all. It is spun exactly as if it were cotton or wool or any one of the natural fibers. Fabrics made from it feel pleasantly soft and "wooly"—very different from the feeling of the smooth fabrics made from filament yarn.

Yet unlike as the two are when made into fabrics, the method of making rayon staple is exactly like that of making the long, smooth strands of filament rayon, until we get to the point in their manufacture where the spinneret is used. At that point, the process begins to be quite different.

In the first place, larger spinnerets with many more holes are used. Then filaments from a number of spinnerets all on one frame are drawn together. They are not twisted, but are made into a continuous loose rope, called a *tow,* which is usually an inch or more in diameter. This tow of filaments is pulled by a tow wheel that feeds into an automatic knife which cuts it into uniform lengths, usually of from one to six inches.

The fact that rayon staple can be cut into different lengths is very important. For it can be cut for use on cotton-spinning machinery which must have one length, or on silk- wool- or worsted-spinning machinery which must have still other lengths.

After it is cut, rayon staple is washed, desulphurized and bleached, and then dried and conditioned in long tunnel dryers. At the far end of the dryers, machines called *openers* fluff up the fibers so that they look very much like cotton.

Like cotton, too, rayon staple is baled for shipping to textile mills which will spin it into yarns known as "spun rayon." Unlike the natural fibers, though, man-made rayon staple is clean when it gets to the mills. It does not have to be sorted, scoured and so on.

Spun rayon is used alone to make a great many different kinds of cloth. It is also very good for blending with short natural fibers like wool and cotton and even with other man-made fibers.

Like continuous-filament yarn, spun rayon yarn is finding more and more uses every day. The scientists who work with rayon are experimenting all the time to turn out better fibers for more and more purposes.

In the United States hundreds of millions of pounds of rayon are produced each year. The fiber that was only a dream three hundred years ago has grown into a huge industry. It has created jobs for vast numbers of Americans. Many of these are highly trained chemists, technicians and other workers in the big companies which make rayon fiber itself. Then there are the mechanics who keep the machinery in order and the salesmen who sell the yarn. More thousands earn their living by knitting, weaving, dyeing and finishing rayon fabrics. Countless others are kept busy supplying the pulp and chemicals needed in rayon manufacture. The fiber whose size, strength, quality and quantity can be controlled by man has brought down the cost of ready-made clothing and made it far more plentiful, attractive and comfortable.

It is impossible to count all the benefits rayon has

brought us. It is easy to see, though, that the long years of scientific searching, the hard work and many disappointments were all wonderfully worth while. For when the chemical laboratory gave rayon, the first man-made fiber, to the loom, it was truly a priceless gift.

This most used of all the man-made fibers is not perfect, however. The ideal fiber has yet to be made. But as the search for it goes on, new wonders are achieved. In the next chapter you will read about the discovery of the amazing fiber that followed rayon.

10: ENTER NYLON

NYLON is so much used and so well known today that many of us may not know what a newcomer it is. Though we have had it only since 1940, most of us take for granted this treasure which science has given us. We'll appreciate our good fortune more when we hear the story of nylon's strange entrance on the textile scene.

We know that the natural fibers—wool, flax, silk and cotton—have been used throughout the ages. And we know that man has constantly added to his knowledge about how best to use them, learning more and more about weaving and knitting and how to dye them. But the quantity and quality of these natural fibers have always been subject to forces that men could not entirely control. Diseases could wipe out great flocks of sheep and millions of silkworms. Blights could wither vast fields of flax and ruin huge cotton plantations. A scarcity of fabrics would, of course, result.

There was little that man could do about the strength, length, weight or thickness of these natural fibers, either. Then, as we know, Chardonnet came and, with his followers, gave the world rayon—a fiber which man could control to a much greater degree than he could any of the natural ones. But rayon, too, had limitations.

One might think that somebody simply realized this and said, "I'm going to invent a fiber that will be the best yet, and I'll call it nylon." But it didn't happen that way. The fact is, the men who found the combination that became nylon were not even looking for a fiber.

How did it happen?

It started in 1927, when the Chemical Director of the du Pont Company started his scientists off on a new kind of research. Instead of searching for things they could turn into useful and valuable products right away, as they had done in the past, this new plan was aimed at learning basic scientific facts that would benefit all chemistry. (This type of research is called fundamental research.)

One of the things the scientists wanted to understand was how and why the small molecules that make up all matter sometimes unite to form "giant" molecules like those that are found in silk, cotton, rubber and many other materials. Such a giant molecule is called a *polymer* which means "many parts." The process of changing from a small molecule to a large one with the same elements in the same proportions is called *polymerization*. For example, cyanuric acid ($C_3N_3O_3H_3$) is a giant molecule, a polymer of cyanic acid (CNOH).

Headed by Dr. Wallace H. Carothers, the du Pont chemists learned that certain small molecules unite to form chainlike molecules of great length—something like paper-clips joined end to end. These are called *linear superpolymers*.

This information was interesting only to other chemists working in the same small field. But after the investigation had been going on for two years, something important happened.

One of the chemists was working with a batch of molten material that belonged to this family of linear superpolymers. When he tried to remove it from the laboratory vessel in which it had been prepared, he noticed that he could draw it out into a long, long fiber —like taffy candy. Then after he cooled it, he found that it could be pulled out to three or four times its original length. In a compound of this kind such a thing had never been seen before.

This queer fiber was not strong, though. Hot water softened it; it wasn't very elastic and it did not look as though it would be good for *anything*. But it was unusual. The chemists thought that if they now searched with a practical purpose as their goal, they might find another compound in this same family that would be useful as a textile fiber. Perhaps they could find one that would be strong, elastic and water-resistant.

So a great many kinds of these superpolymers were

created and each one was tested. But every single one had something wrong with it which made it imprac-tical for textiles. After months and months of work without any success, the scientists stopped looking. They didn't forget the whole thing, however, and when they again started work on the idea, they made a new type of polymer called a *polyamide*. They took some of this polymer and squirted it out of a hypodermic needle. This time they produced the first fiber of the kind now known as nylon. This was the first truly synthetic fiber. (Synthetic means a compound which is built up by combining other compounds or their elements.) The rayons are products of wood and cotton converted to another form. But nylon is a completely new chemical compound, a new molecule unlike any that exists in any form in plants or animals, in minerals or in any form of nature.

Squirting the nylon polymer from a hypodermic needle was a crude way to make a fiber. But from the very first tests this fiber looked so promising that unusual efforts were made to get it out of the laboratory and into the stores quickly. A large force of chemists and chemical engineers was put on the job. But it took years! Finally the research staff developed a polyamide which they called "66." Though many different types have since been made and studied, it is still the "66" variety that is most used for textiles. And it was "66" that was used in the first product to be sold throughout the country: toothbrushes with nylon bristles. These were introduced to the American public in the fall of 1938—nearly ten whole years from the day that the first studies were started on polymerization.

Compare the size of a toothbrush bristle with the finest fiber of a fine thread, and you will agree that it is like comparing a broomstick with a toothpick. So the chemists who had developed a new polymer knew that though the first big step had been taken toward a wonderful new textile, there were still many problems to solve before they could present sheer nylon stockings or fine nylon dresses, nylon shirts, nylon slips and underwear to the public.

Instead of little test-tube amounts, they had to find a way to make this new material in freight-car and train-load quantities. This meant that chemical engineers and architects had to design complete new manufacturing plants. New machinery had to be devised. New land had to be used, new buildings had to be constructed. Laborers, technicians, even chemists had to be hired and trained to work with this brand-new material. Even after all this work was done, the chemists made only the nylon yarn. So the weavers, dyers and finishers, the stocking manufacturers, the underwear makers, the shirtmakers and all those who might use the yarn and the woven cloth would still have to learn how to use this new material.

While stocking manufacturers learned to handle nylon yarn in a small experimental "pilot plant" which was set up for that purpose, the first large-scale factory was started early in 1939. Late that year the first nylon-yarn spinning machine went into operation. On May 15, 1940, all over the country nylon hosiery at last went on sale. It was a sensation. Every woman wanted the stockings that were the sheerest ever seen, yet were strong and long-wearing.

Many must have bought them, too, before nylon went to war soon after Pearl Harbor and none could be got for civilian use. For, a little later, patriotic women turned in over seven million pairs of stockings for scrap.

After the war ended, more nylon plants were built and many new uses for the wonderful fiber were found. The nylon industry has grown constantly ever since. Today nylon and the other man-made fibers are chemistry's biggest industry.

Since nylon is a true test-tube fiber, made chemically from the start, its manufacture is quite different from that of rayon. The chemicals that the nylon factory starts with are made from raw materials such as coal, air and water. But between these familiar things and the finished yarn there are many long, complicated steps. Here is how the du Pont Company describes the process:

1. As the diagram shows, the process is a highly complex one. Two chemicals called *hexamethylene diamine* and *adipic acid* are made by a series of chemical steps. They are then combined, and the resultant product is called *nylon salt*.

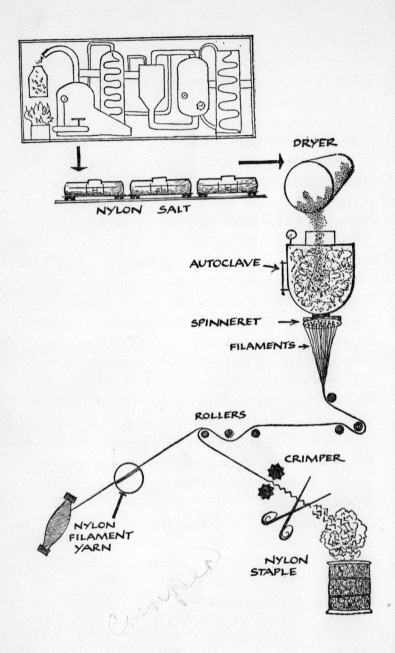

NYLON SALT

DRYER

AUTOCLAVE

SPINNERET

FILAMENTS

ROLLERS

CRIMPER

NYLON FILAMENT YARN

NYLON STAPLE

2. For ease in handling, the salt is dissolved in water and shipped to other du Pont plants for manufacture into textile fibers, bristles and other forms.

3. To make fibers, the first step is to evaporate a portion of the water from the salt.

4. The salt is then placed in an *autoclave,* a piece of equipment like a giant pressure cooker. Here the remaining water is driven off and heat combines the molecules of the two chemicals into the giant ones, the linear polymers.

5. Nylon fibers are then made by pumping the hot, molten nylon out through tiny holes in a *spinneret,* which is a metal disc about the size of a silver dollar. The holes are so small that you can see them only by holding the spinneret up to a strong light. The number of holes in a spinneret can be varied to suit the purpose for which the yarn is made.

6. Here a yarn made with several filaments is being spun. As the filaments hit the air, they solidify, and are then gathered together to become a yarn.

7. Next the yarn is stretched, or *drawn,* between a system of rollers. The arrangement of the linear molecules is changed from a haphazard one to an orderly arrangement in which the molecules are lined up parallel to the axis of the filaments. It is this drawing process that gives elasticity and great strength to the finished yarn.

8. The drawn filament yarn, after being carefully inspected, is then ready for shipment.

9. Nylon staple is made by crimping continuous

nylon filaments and then cutting them into short, uniform lengths. It is shipped in large 500-pound packs much like bales of cotton.

There are three types of nylon yarn. Multifilament yarn is composed of many tiny, almost endless filaments or strands twisted together into one yarn. Most nylon fabrics are made of this type, and in all of them

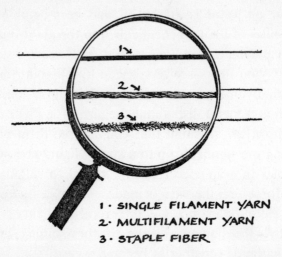

1 · SINGLE FILAMENT YARN
2 · MULTIFILAMENT YARN
3 · STAPLE FIBER

this multifilament yarn gives pleasant surface texture, softness and good draping qualities.

Single-filament yarn is composed of just one solid strand of great smoothness and strength. This is used for very sheer hosiery, for veils and for blouses and gowns.

Staple is made from many short, wavy strands of nylon cut in lengths from one-half to five inches. The wave or "crimp" in the filaments of this yarn adds springiness and makes light, soft fabrics that are pleasing to the touch. This yarn is popular for sweaters and socks.

Because nylon does not take dyes in the same way as the natural fibers do, there were special problems to be solved in dyeing it. Some entirely new techniques had to be developed.

Every girl has seen a party dress or a skirt with pre-set pleats that don't come out when the dress is washed. This is done by *heat-setting*—pleating with unusually high heat. Then the pleats won't come out unless the fabric is subjected to even higher heat.

But the really outstanding feature of nylon is the unusual strength which is given it by the "drawing" operation described in the seventh step in the manufacturing process. A filament of nylon that has been made with very slight pull can be drawn out from four to seven times its original length, depending on the kind of polyamide used. When it is correctly drawn out, nylon has a combination of strength and elasticity that is greater than that of any other textile fiber in common use.

Nylon is tough, too. This quality makes it good for bristles in hair brushes, clothes brushes and paint brushes, which will last at least three times as long as natural bristles from hogs.

Nylon absorbs much less water than other textile fibers. That's why it dries out so quickly after washing. And that is also why nylon bristles are much less affected by moisture than natural hog bristles.

Because nylon fibers are smooth, they do not soil

easily, and dirt can be quickly removed. Soap and water and dry cleaning fluids will not hurt nylon in the least.

Normally, moths, silverfish and other insects will not attack nylon, as the nylon itself has no attraction for them. Mildew may form on nylon under some of the same conditions as on other fibers. But mildew will not weaken nylon fabric.

For many industrial and commercial uses, nylon has given better service and has proven to be cheaper than other materials. Its strength, toughness and many other properties make it better than older materials for making such sea-going gear as the cargo nets used in loading ships, and those giant-size ropes, the tugboat hawsers, that tow and guide big liners and freighters. Other dramatic uses of nylon are in parachutes and parachute cords, used so much by our troops in wartime. But nylon takes to the air in other ways, too. Airplane propellers, for example, sometimes ice up in flight, and when they do, planes get the shakes and lose a great deal of power. Designers solved the problem by protecting the leading edge of propellers with an electrically heated fabric skin of nylon. When ice builds up, the pilot turns on the heat in the fabric and away goes the ice, restoring the plane to calm flight and the propeller to full power. The thinness of the nylon fabric maintains the efficiency of the propeller in normal use, and the strength of the fabric resists the centrifugal force that constantly tries to rip it off.

Bottle brushes, dry cleaners' brushes that have to

withstand all kinds of cleaning fluids, racquet strings, guitar and other musical instrument strings, fishing leaders, fishing nets, surgical sutures and dozens of other products are now made with nylon instead of with the natural fibers used in the past.

The first pound of nylon is said to have cost $27,000,000 to make. But the tremendous success and wide usefulness of this first truly synthetic textile fiber shows once again how greatly scientific research can benefit mankind.

For such work, however, highly trained scientists and technicians are needed. Today the demand for them is far greater than the supply. In many branches of science there is fine opportunity for those who can qualify.

To see what qualities are ideal for those who wish to make science their life work, here is a short biographical sketch of a distinguished scientist:

Descended from farming people and the son of a teacher, he was a great reader as a boy. He was enthusiastic about work and about play, too. He liked tools and mechanical things. He spent a lot of time experimenting. In public school his work was thorough. He never left a job half-finished or carelessly done. In college he specialized in chemistry, which he taught during his junior and senior years to help pay for his education. Friends who remember him in his young student days speak of his mature judgment, his wide interests, his love of music. He liked people. He was quiet, methodical, careful and systematic. He was an original thinker and liked independent research problems. He received the degree of B.S. (Bachelor of Science) when he graduated from college, and he went on to earn the degrees of M.A. (Master of Arts) and Ph.D. (Doctor of Philosophy). He worked in organic chemistry, physical chemistry and mathematics, and taught inorganic chemistry and other subjects. He was a popular and excellent teacher and later a brilliant research scientist. Though he received wide acclaim, he was always modest. He was absorbed in his work, yet had a wide knowledge of politics, labor problems, business, art and philosophy. His hobby was a fine collection of phonograph records.

Who was he? Dr. Wallace Hume Carothers, the man on whose remarkable studies and work the duPont Company based the experiments which finally produced nylon.

11: MORE WONDER FABRICS

NYLON'S success started a race among chemical manufacturers all over the world for textile fibers that might compete with nylon or might serve purposes that nylon couldn't. Chemists in many other companies were working on the same problems, but du Pont seemed to have a head start, since they had set up their research program on the polymers so long before and had so many people working on it.

The result was that in 1950 they came up with a second truly synthetic fiber which they called "Orlon." It is known by textile chemists as an *acrylic* fiber and it is made from a compound which, in turn, is made from such raw materials as coal, air, water, petroleum, limestone and natural gases.

Not long after Orlon came on the market, two other big companies announced that they, too, had some acrylic fibers for sale. Union Carbide & Carbon Company presented "Dynel"; Monsanto Chemical joined American Viscose and built the $30,000,000 Chemstrand Corporation plant for the manufacture of "Acri-

121

lan." All three of these products are acrylic fibers. They belong to the same general family, have some of the same virtues and faults, but each is an entirely different chemical compound.

Orlon, Dynel and Acrilan fabrics are quick-drying, long-wearing, shrink-resistant, mothproof, mildew-proof, and wrinkle-resistant. They can be warm yet light in weight, need little or no ironing, will hold permanent pleats, and have a pleasing texture (what textile people call "a warm, dry hand"). This is what the scientists had been looking for: some of the things that natural silk had to offer, some that only wool had had, and some that none of the natural fibers could supply.

These three newest synthetics are used alone or in combination with other yarns to make many attractive fabrics, including bright satins, taffetas and velvets.

Men's shirts made of Orlon, Dynel or Acrilan are comfortable and good-looking, and they require a very small amount of care, since they can be laundered and dried quickly and need little if any ironing. Sweaters made with these fibers won't shrink or stretch; they keep their shape, need no blocking, and won't be chewed up by moths. Topcoats and overcoats of these materials can be surprisingly light, yet warm. They drape well, tailor well, and any wrinkles will hang out. After wetting, garments dry out in a hurry. In cold climates "woolies" made of feather-soft yarns of these fibers feel pleasant to the skin. They are warm, never scratchy, wash readily, dry quickly, won't stretch or shrink and need no ironing.

Orlon is made from the chemical called *acrylonitrile*. Again, as in the making of nylon, we come to that big word *polymerization,* which, you remember, refers to the change of small molecules into big molecules. The acrylonitrile is polymerized in a container with water and a catalyst. A catalyst is a chemical element or compound that remains unchanged but must be present in order to bring about the reaction wanted. (It is a little like the hostess at a party who has to introduce people to each other, but is so busy doing that, that she can't do anything else.)

The newly formed chemical comes out of the container in solid form, and is cut into pieces that look like broken-up noodles. Its name is *polyacrylonitrile*. (Maybe you'll find that word easier to think of, if you break it into pieces, like this: *poly, acrylo, nitrile*.) This is the actual chemical composition of Orlon. But to put it into useful fiber form, it must be spun. This, in turn, requires a semiliquid form. So the polyacrylonitrile is dissolved and, after some other steps, it is pumped through the spinneret, then drawn and made into either continuous-filament yarn, or cut and crimped into staple before shipment to the textile mills.

As with the nylon process, this brief description may sound (except for the long words) as though the making of Orlon is really quite simple. To a scientist who has spent years studying and working in that particular field of chemistry, it might seem so, too. But there are many steps in making each of the compounds that go into these products, and each step requires careful control. No, it is not simple, and must be directed by people who have studied and worked a long time in acquiring their skill.

Dynel and Acrilan are the products of many chemical steps, too, and both depend on acrylonitrile as one of the ingredients of the final fiber. "Saran," which is made by Dow Chemical Company, depends on some of the same raw materials, but does not use acrylonitrile. Saran is used for such things as tough bus seats, the "threads" being heavy, single-filament yarn woven like cane or reed chair seats. (You may have seen a transparent film made of this material—it is known as "Saran Wrap" and is widely used for wrapping foods.)

In the chapter on nylon, you read about Dr. Wallace H. Carothers, who directed the fundamental research that led eventually to nylon. It was Dr. Carothers' work with polymers that laid the groundwork for "Dacron," too. But this fiber came to America by quite a different route.

Among the first polymers which Dr. Carothers studied were *polyesters*. Esters, we should know, are compounds formed by the action of alcohol and an acid. They are widely used and some are easily recognized in perfumes and in flavorings by the experienced chemist. Dr. Carothers dropped the study of the polyesters when he changed to the polyamides which led to the development of nylon. But for the benefit of scientists everywhere, he published what he had found out. When some British research chemists read Carothers' report, they continued the study of polyesters.

Their work resulted in the development of a polyester fiber which they called "Terylene," a name which they evidently made up from parts of the names of the raw materials used: *dimethyl terephthalate* and *ethylene glycol*.

When they learned what the British scientists had developed, du Pont bought their patent rights and produced it here. They call it "Dacron."

In the Dacron process the two raw materials are added to a container, and polymerization is brought about at a high temperature, using a vacuum. Like nylon, the resulting material is spun while it is still in its hot, molten state. The filaments are stretched about four times their original length to give them strength.

Dacron is unusually resilient and springs back to its original position after crushing or bending, whether it is wet or dry. This makes it highly resistant to wrinkling and gives it the ability to recover quickly when it has been wrinkled by hard use.

Like nylon, Dacron can be preset to a good crease under heat and pressure; once the fiber has been "bent" this way, it stays. You can wash it and, even when it is mixed with wool, you can spot-clean it with soap and water without harm to shape, size or the resiliency of the fiber. It is tough and durable and stands up to the kind of hard wear that suits and slacks get in such places as cuffs, pockets and trouser seats.

Some other man-made fibers have also been quite successful. In Italy, Lanital is made of milk casein; in the United States, Vicara is made from corn and Ardil from peanuts. Instead of being made from a cellulose base like the rayons, these three are made from another natural product—proteins. The protein fibers are known as *Azlons*. Like the rayons, they are man-made but they are not synthetics.

A recent addition to the textile scene is the non-woven fabric. Paper and felt are familiar examples of nonwoven materials. Their short fibers are placed by chance so that they point in every direction—not just at right angles to each other like the fibers in all woven materials. With pressure and moisture, the fibers of wood pulp or wool interlock to make paper or wool fabric.

Within the last few years several companies have added something to the ancient art of making paper and felt. First they space out one set of parallel threads of rayon, nylon, glass or any other kind. These are coated with an adhesive. Then another set of parallel threads is placed at right angles to the first set, and bonded together by means of high pressure and heat to form a grid or web. Then on each side of this web, fibers of any variety can be laid out to form either a flat or a wooly surface, and they, too, are bonded with heat and pressure.

These materials have become very popular for interlinings of coats and suits, and some are being used for outer wear as well. Within a few short years, production has grown from almost nothing to millions of pounds annually.

What about the future? Will we keep on seeing one new fiber after another come on the market? It seems safe to say that only if a fiber is found that is as good as those now in use—*and* cheaper to make—will it come on the market to stay.

Although the perfect fiber still has not been discovered, we now have different fibers with almost all of the characteristics that anyone could ask for. The number of blends and combinations of fibers that can be made is nearly endless. This is clear when we realize that two, three or more fibers may be blended together in a single yarn and that any number of different kinds of yarns can be woven together in an almost limitless number of combinations.

The success of the test-tube fibers has spurred the natural-fiber industries on to put a great deal of money and effort into finding new ways of treating their fibers so that they will be more satisfactory than ever before. Though natural and man-made fibers may compete, they often team up with great success. Since there is no such thing as an all-purpose fiber, the blending of fibers is often the answer.

It looks as if the textile experts' job from now on will be to find blends and combinations of fibers that will be ideal for the uses to which they are put.

12: GLASS AND RUBBER

FOR centuries the word *glass* has meant something breakable and brittle. Drop a delicate drinking glass on a concrete floor and anyone knows what is likely to happen. With that picture in mind, glass thread and glass cloth seemed, until this century, like a complete impossibility.

Many centuries ago the Phoenicians took balls of molten glass and stretched them into long strings. They were probably the first fibers of glass made with a purpose in mind. The purpose, though, was only decoration—not thread or cloth.

Late in the 1920's the Germans made glass fibers on a commercial scale, but these, too, were just for decoration and were so highly irregular in every way that they could not be used for thread or fabric.

In the 1930's one of our glass companies began to look for new ways to use glass, new ways to employ people, new ways to keep their factories busy in a period of depression. Among the first things they made were air filters for heating and air-conditioning systems. They were made of glass fibers and were so cheap that they could be thrown away when they got dirty.

Soon after that, they made building insulation of coarse glass fibers. Then, improving their methods, they made fine, blown "glass wool," which later on was used for insulating the hundreds of ships that were so rapidly built during World War II. And finally the glass companies learned how to make fine, uniform fibers for textile use.

Before you read how they are made, you ought to know how "brittle, breakable" glass can be flexible enough to be used as yarn.

Press your thumb against a small pane of window glass and it won't budge. But push gently against the center of a large plate of glass in a big store window and you can see from the reflections that it bends a surprising distance even though it may be a quarter of an inch thick. The thinner the window, the more it would bend.

Think now of a glass cylinder—a glass stirring rod. You can't see the bend in a short length very easily. But a long piece bends readily, and the smaller the diameter, the more it will bend. And so it is that when glassmakers draw out their fibers so fine that single filaments can hardly be seen without a microscope, the fibers are amazingly pliable.

In one process, glass is first made by mixing about 55 per cent sand, 16 per cent alumina, 20 per cent lime and 10 per cent boric oxides. This is melted to make the first product—glass marbles about three quarters of an inch in diameter. They are inspected, tested and then rolled into an electric crucible which is a very special kind of melting pot. This one doesn't use a flame; it doesn't use an electric arc, which is the little cousin of lightning. This is a round crucible that is surrounded by, but never touched by, an induction heating coil. The coil gets very warm, but never as hot as the materials inside the crucible. It directs electric currents into the material itself, which is heated very evenly throughout its whole mass.

When the glass is hot enough, small filaments from 204 holes in the bottom of the crucible are pulled out at a speed of about 120 miles an hour, stretching and thinning them to diameters of tenths of thousandths of an inch. How thick? Well, draw a circle 2¾ inches in diameter. Let that represent the thickness of an average human hair as you would see it under a microscope. That hair is about 1/1000 of an inch in diameter. Now draw another circle ½ inch in diameter and you can compare the human hair with the size of some of the smaller glass filaments: 2/10,000 of an inch thick.

Glass fabrics made from yarns spun from such fibers as these are of great value in electrical work, among other things. When an electric motor is made with wire that is insulated with glass fiber, the motor can stand a great deal of heat without damage. Also, the size of the motor can be smaller for the same amount of power, since glass insulation requires less space than some other kinds.

For homes and offices, glass-fiber curtains and draperies have the advantage of being fireproof, rotproof, mildew-proof, and resistant to nearly all chemicals.

When they are sandwiched with layers of plastics, glass fabrics lend amazing strength and toughness to such things as plastic boats and the radomes that cover the radar equipment in modern aircraft. They have been used in some experimental auto bodies with considerable success, and in many industrial parts.

In many fabrics, the glass fiber is coated with a plastic which prevents the fibers from cutting or "sandpapering" each other and anything else they might touch.

Glass yarns have tremendous strength, and when they are woven together with yarns of other fibers they add strength to the entire fabric. They will not shrink and, since they will not absorb water, they can be washed and dried in record time. Curtains of glass cloth can be washed and rehung in a matter of minutes, and they won't sag or stretch.

When "superfine" glass wool is to be made, glass filaments are run through a gas flame where they are melted and blown into the air above and beyond the flame. This flame-blowing changes the filaments to diameters of hundredths of thousandths of an inch. While flying through the air, the glass is coated with resinous compounds blown into the chamber with the filaments. These compounds will bind the filaments together. The fibers are allowed to settle on a screen to form a loose mat or blanket. This blanket is then baked to harden the resin binder, and the blanket is then rolled up, ready to ship to those who will use it. It is light and fluffy and will stay resilient and hold its shape permanently because of the binder. If you pile up pieces of it to make a cube one foot on each edge, some types will weigh only half a pound.

This is the material that is used within the walls of your refrigerator as insulation to help keep it cold; in the cabins of airplanes to keep them quiet and to keep you comfortably warm or cool in flight. It is used for sound- and heat-insulation in dozens of other products, too. Sandwiched with plastics, it was used to make bullet-proof vests during the Korean war. Coated with water-repellent chemicals, it makes an ideal life preserver, for it will never rot, no matter how long it stays unused in a ship's locker. Do you want to see some of this glass wool? Many big hardware stores sell it for sound- or heat-insulation at home, and you can buy it an inch thick, a couple of feet wide, and as long as you want it.

Rubber

When the first researchers were trying to find an "artificial silk," they wanted it to be as nearly like natural silk as possible. The searchers for a rubber substitute had the same kind of idea.

For years chemists tried to duplicate rubber as they

had matched perfumes, dyes and flavors with exactly the same chemical structures. But they failed just as the silk copyists had failed. They tried to break the rubber structure into its chemical parts and then put it together again. Nobody will ever know all the thousands of hours that chemists throughout the world spent on this problem. But finally they stopped trying to duplicate nature, and began juggling molecules in an effort to find something completely new.

What they developed—from petroleum gases, alcohol, coke, limestone and salt—was an elastic material that was in some ways as good as natural rubber, in others not as good. But even more important, it could do some things that natural rubber could never do.

If you put natural rubber in oil or gasoline, it rots. But synthetic rubber made by science was used to line the inside of gasoline tanks of fighter planes and bombers, so that bullets could go right through them without leaving terrible trails of flaming gasoline behind them; instead, the holes in the synthetic rubber would seal themselves.

Soon other kinds of synthetic rubber were made, including the kind so widely used in automobile tires, beginning before World War II.

Since that time a great variety of synthetic rubbers have been developed to do all kinds of special jobs, from cutting down vibration in railway cars to making collapsible 55-gallon rubber drums for shipping liquids. When the liquids have been used, one freight car can carry twenty-five hundred of these back to the factory for re-use, compared to only three hundred metal drums.

Synthetic rubber threads can be made by cutting thin sheets into narrow strips or by pumping the solution through a spinneret in the same manner as other man-made fibers are formed. Yarns of synthetic rubber can be used without covering, but for use in clothing they are usually covered with cotton, rayon, nylon or other fiber.

In elastic waistbands and for other uses, the synthetic rubber has been so perfected that it is odorless, will make 100 per cent recovery after violent stretching, will resist heat, age and sunlight far better than natural rubber. The effect of detergents and cleaning fluids varies with the type of rubber used.

There is a wide variety of fabrics in which rubber is used. Cords, braids, girdles, surgical stockings, suspenders, garters, sock tops, bands over the instep of women's shoes, and sporting goods are all familiar.

Less familiar, but economically more important, are the industrial uses of rubberized fabrics, as in escalators, power transmission belts such as the automobile fan belt, water hoses, conveyor belts and dozens of other machine parts.

13: WHICH SHALL I CHOOSE?

THE appeal of "artificial silk," as rayon was first called, was its rich, lustrous appearance. But by the time of World War II and the development of newer fibers, textile people had found that man-made fibers offer many things that are more important than their looks.

It would be fine, of course, if one fiber would change magically whenever you wanted it to. But everybody knows you can't make a good raincoat out of a bath towel or a good bath towel by tearing a raincoat into flat pieces. We have to choose the fiber (and the weave and the processing) to fit the job we want done.

Before the man-made fibers were developed, we had only a few natural ones from which to choose. Today if there is a job that none of our fibers will do, scientists can begin to hunt for the ideal new fiber or combination of fibers for the job, with some real hope of finding it.

What are some of the jobs to be done? What does it take to do them? The towel and the raincoat illustrate needs that are direct opposites. The towel's job is to drink up water like a thirsty horse. The raincoat's job is to shed water like a duck in a thundershower. Those are the most important jobs to be done, of course. But there would be many other things to think about if you were going to *make* a bath towel or a raincoat, instead of only going to a store to buy it.

You want a towel that is soft, that launders easily, that holds its shape, that stays white as snow or keeps its color if it has been dyed. Then too, it must be strong when it is wet as well as when it is dry. It should absorb about four times its own weight in water. Its surface should return to the original appearance and feeling after each washing. When you shake it, it must not shed lint as a prairie storm sheds dust.

Here are some of the requirements for raincoat material, besides the ability to hold its shape: it must stay dry as a desert; it must absorb no water, or at least so little that it is scarcely noticeable; it must be strong, whether wet or dry; it must not soil easily; the original yarn must be easy to dye and must hold its color.

It is clear that no one fiber or weave can be perfect for two things as different as a bath towel and a raincoat. Fibers must be specially treated by manufacturers for the different jobs they are to do.

Hundreds of other uses for fibers call for other features, such as warmth in winter; coolness in summer clothes; extreme strength and stretch in the fiber cords built into auto and truck tires and airplane landing-wheel tires; long-wearing quality in upholstery fabrics for auto, bus, train and airplane seats; fire resistance for curtains and draperies in theaters, restaurants and other public places.

When all these qualities have been named, it is not so hard to choose the fibers that will best do the job. But even the best may not be perfect. To make a good choice you ought to know a great many facts. What makes wool warm in winter? What makes cotton and rayon cool in summer? What do we know about the wearing quality of cottons, woolens, rayons or other fabrics? These, too, are some of the questions scientists have to answer when they start to search for the best fiber for any job.

As we have seen in the chapter on the spinning and weaving of natural fibers, many fibers are partly twisted around each other to form yarn. The yarn, of course, is then woven to make the textile.

Now one of the first things that a textile expert wants to know about any yarn is: how strong is it?

When engineers talk about tensile strength of metals they usually refer to the weight that a one-inch-square bar will hold suspended in mid-air before it breaks, or the equivalent of that strength as they measure it with their testing machines in a laboratory. But yarns, obviously, are not made in one-inch-square bars, and different yarns of the same thickness are quite different in weight. This is an important thing in clothes.

When you compare equal lengths of the same diameter of rayon and nylon thread, for example, you will find that rayon weighs nearly one and a half times as

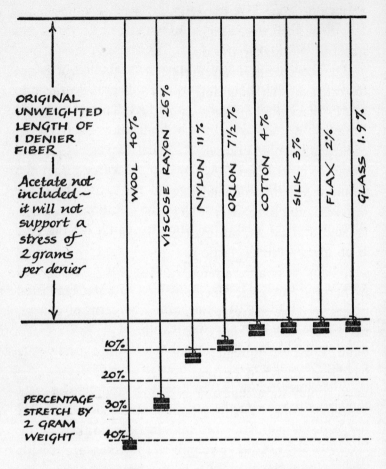

ORIGINAL UNWEIGHTED LENGTH OF 1 DENIER FIBER

Acetate not included ~ it will not support a stress of 2 grams per denier

WOOL 40%

VISCOSE RAYON 26%

NYLON 11%

ORLON 7½%

COTTON 4%

SILK 3%

FLAX 2%

GLASS 1.9%

PERCENTAGE STRETCH BY 2 GRAM WEIGHT

10%

20%

30%

40%

much as nylon. So to make the measurements useful, textile scientists refer to a combination of weight and length known as the *denier*. A one-denier yarn is a 9,000-meter length of yarn that weighs one gram. (A meter is 39.37 inches. To understand how much a gram is, imagine a little ice cube .3937 inch on each side— slightly more than three eighths of an inch. This weighs about one gram.) A two-denier yarn is a 9,000-meter length of yarn that weighs two grams. And so on. In general, the higher the denier, the stronger the yarn.

The comparative strength of various fibers is illustrated in the diagram. It shows the relative distances that different fibers would be stretched by equal forces.

Strength alone, however, is just one of the important things to be considered when you choose a fabric. The value of any fiber depends also on its ability to return to its original form after it has been pulled and pushed, twisted, walked on, sat on or pressed down in any way. If all fibers were as elastic as rubber bands, they would snap back, after a big stretch, to exactly the same length as before. But some fibers are far more elastic than others, and the recovery of some of them to their original form is not so quick as the recovery of a rubber band. For even though a fiber may look as though it has been stretched beyond repair, if you examine it later, it may show that time is a great healer—even for a stretched fiber. Textile scientists know that by a slow process that they do not completely understand, a recovery is made that is far greater than would be expected. For example, a badly mussed pair of wool slacks, after being properly hung up for a time, will almost entirely recover its shape without being pressed.

It is, then, the combination of its strength and its elasticity that tells a large part of the story of the usefulness of any fiber. Wool is weak, compared to most other fibers, but its elasticity makes it very practical

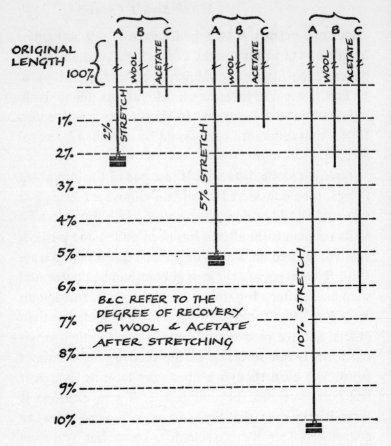

ORIGINAL LENGTH { 100%

A   B   C   A   B   C   A   B   C

WOOL ACETATE   WOOL ACETATE   WOOL ACETATE

2% STRETCH

5% STRETCH

10% STRETCH

1% —
2% —
3% —
4% —
5% —
6% —
7% —
8% —
9% —
10% —

B & C REFER TO THE
DEGREE OF RECOVERY
OF WOOL & ACETATE
AFTER STRETCHING

for many things, as we all know. Glass fiber, on the other hand, has terrific strength, but it cannot be stretched very far without breaking. This limits its usefulness greatly. Luckily, other fibers stand somewhere between these two extremes. Nylon, for example, has both high strength and great elasticity. Because this is so, nylon, as we know, can be used for many purposes.

The combination of strength and elasticity has much to do with wearing quality, too. But there are other reasons for good or poor wearing quality in a finished textile, such as the form of the yarn or the kind of weave that is used in the textile itself. Wool yarn, for example, is almost never as smooth as rayon yarn. When the fuzzier surface of wool trousers or skirts touches the seat of a chair, it is like the bristle side of a brush in its many, many points of contact. Each bristle acts like a tiny spring. But an acetate rayon yarn is more like the smooth back of a brush when it touches the seat of a chair, simply because it does not have nearly so many points of contact. Wool "rolls with the punches" in effect, recovering quickly from thousands of tiny stresses. Rayon presents a smoother surface and does not recover nearly so well from the pressures it has to withstand. From this you can see that rayon does not wear as well as wool.

But clothing must hold its size and shape besides usually being required to wear well. Men and boys don't like trousers with baggy knees; women and girls don't like blouses and skirts that become as shapeless as old sacks. Nor does anyone want clothes that shrink to a size that would fit only a midget.

There are two kinds of shrinkage. One, known as *swelling shrinkage,* happens when water is absorbed into spaces between the molecules, of which a fiber, like all other matter, is made up. This makes each tiny fiber thicker, and at the same time shortens its length. This, in turn, shrinks the entire woven fabric. It is this kind of shrinkage that occurs in wool, cotton, silk, linen, rayon and the Azlon fibers. But it does not happen to nylon,

Dacron or any of the other man-made fibers of their kind because they will not, they cannot, absorb water in their molecules.

The second kind of water shrinkage is called *relaxation shrinkage*. This is the sort of thing that happens when you throw a crumpled piece of crisp paper into water—all the springiness of the paper goes limp. Just so, the fibers that have been pulled and twisted together, combed, wound, shuttled and steamed through all the processes from spinning to final textile, will relax and tend to return to their original positions when they are put in water. The hotter the water is, the greater will the relaxation be. This explains why you should wash wool socks and sweaters in cool water to keep them in good condition. With the exception of glass fabric, all fabrics, whether man-made or natural, will change their shapes to some extent from relaxation shrinkage.

But shrinking may be controlled in several ways. For cotton, there is the well-known process of Sanforizing, which is simply the deliberate, controlled shrinking of the woven textile before it is made up in the form of a shirt, dress or other final product. Sanforizing does not use chemicals. It is purely a mechanical process.

Chemical ways of control may be used for wool and rayon. The fibers are treated with one of the resins in its liquid form. Then the treated fibers are heated to bring about the last stage of the chemical reaction of the resin which changes it to a solid. Dry cleaning and laundering can afterward remove only small amounts of the resin, which stays within the fiber and keeps it—and therefore the woven fabric—in shape.

A third way of preventing shrinkage is by combining fibers that do not shrink in water with those that do—Dacron with wool, Dynel with cotton, etc. The result, of course, is that the nonshrinking fibers tend to keep the whole woven fabric in shape.

This same method is used to prevent wrinkling— combining wool with Dacron, and other mixtures. But scientists are still searching for some answers to the problem of preventing wrinkling. Richard Armour's verse puts it this way:

> The crease and the wrinkle, there isn't much doubt,
> Are alike in a number of ways,
> But the crease is the one that so quickly comes out,
> While the wrinkle's the one that stays.

One way of "building in" resistance to wrinkling is by using fabrics made of thin yarns that have been tightly twisted. This gives the cloth an unusually springy structure that tends to snap back to its original shape far more readily than ordinary fabrics.

"Permanent" pleats are possible in nylon, as almost everyone knows who has seen any of the many-pleated nylon skirts. Orlon and Dynel fabrics, too, can be made with these "permanent" pleats because all three of these fibers have what is known as a "heat memory." When any of these fabrics are pleated or creased, they tend to hold that crease unless they are heated to higher temperatures. The manufacturers put the original pleats in the fabrics at temperatures much higher than any the fabrics are likely to have to stand in the home, in the laundry, or in the tailor's or dry cleaning shop.

So far we have talked about appearance, strength, wearing quality, shrinking and so on. But we haven't mentioned one of the most important things about fibers for clothing. That is comfort. What makes a fabric warm in winter or cool in summer, "just right" in the house, or "just right" when you are out in a blizzard?

Even the scientists don't know *all* the answers. But here is a start. We all know that when the temperature is a moderate 68°, we may feel that it is much too hot in muggy, sticky weather, or too cold for us to sit still on bright, dry days. To know why one fiber is good and another not so good in these different conditions, we must think how fibers insulate, and also what these fibers and different weaves do with the moisture of the air and the moisture that comes from the pores of our skin.

The insulating quality of a fabric depends first on its ability to trap air between its fibers. To continue its usefulness as an insulator, the fabric must not pack down in use, for this—by crushing the fibers closer together—would destroy the insulating air spaces and so destroy its value.

It is the high elasticity of wool which prevents it from packing down and accounts for its long service as a warm fabric year after year. Many other fibers can be made into fabrics that are just as warm as wool *during their first use;* but without wool's elasticity, most other fibers will pack down and the fabric will lose its thousands of insulating air traps and become almost useless.

But insulation is not the only job required for the regulation of our body temperature. We depend greatly on the proper rate of evaporation of perspiration for our comfort, and our clothing must supply the ways for regulating that rate. Let's see what some of these ways are.

Wool, cotton and rayon absorb water readily. In clothing, these fibers allow the removal of perspiration from our skin in two ways. First, they permit the escape of perspiration in the form of water vapor between the yarns of the woven fabric. And second, liquid perspiration is absorbed directly by the fibers of the cloth, which transfer it to the outer surface of the cloth in exactly the same way that oil is carried up a wick in an old-fashioned oil lamp. We shall call these two ways of removing perspiration the *air route* and the *wick route*.

In normal conditions the air route is the only route possible for the nonabsorbent fibers such as Dynel and nylon. Fabrics made of these fibers must be thin or loosely woven if the air route is to stay open. But when winds blow, thin, porous fabrics will allow the skin to cool too quickly. Or if the sun is very bright they do not protect the skin from sunburn.

When we wear a shirt made of one of the nonabsorbent fibers like nylon or Dynel, it may feel very comfortable for a minute or two of physical exercise. But if we go on exercising and perspiration is produced rapidly, it may not escape at the same speed and we become most uncomfortable. Because cotton, wool and rayon absorb moisture in their fibers and carry it by the wick route to the outer air, where it can evaporate, and because at the same time they allow passage of water vapor by the air route, they are likely to be more comfortable for such uses.

For outer garments for work and sports, however, man-made fibers like nylon have definite advantages. They can be wind-resistant. They resist a kind of sandpapering motion, called abrasion, and they are light in weight.

With so many different and wonderful fabrics in today's world, perhaps you are thinking: "When I go shopping, which one shall I choose?" Now that you have read this far, though, you know that your choice will be almost entirely decided by the use to which you intend to put your new fabric or garment.

If it is to be for a swim suit, you will want the cloth to be reasonably light in weight, quick-drying and colorfast. But probably you will not mind very much if it wears out after one season. A fabric made of cotton, rayon, a blend, or any one of several of the new synthetics would be attractive and practical, too.

Perhaps, though, you will soon be shopping for a

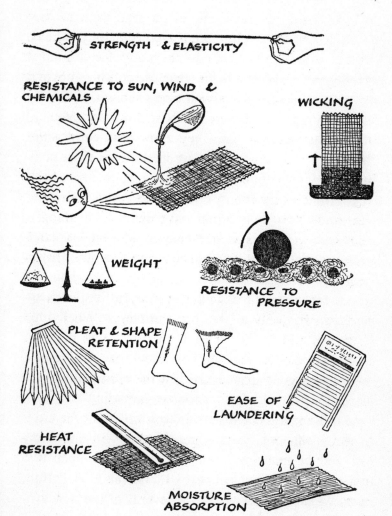

STRENGTH & ELASTICITY

RESISTANCE TO SUN, WIND & CHEMICALS

WICKING

WEIGHT

RESISTANCE TO PRESSURE

PLEAT & SHAPE RETENTION

EASE OF LAUNDERING

HEAT RESISTANCE

MOISTURE ABSORPTION

winter coat instead of for the far less expensive swim suit. If that's the case, and if you are like most of us, you'll not only want your new coat to fit well and to be stylish, but you will also want it to be durable enough to last several years, either for you or for a younger member of your family to wear. Firm, closely woven or knit fabrics usually give the best service. If the coat is simply made and the color is soft or dark, you will like it much longer than if it is extreme in cut or color. Be sure to know your present correct size and ask for it. But try the coat on for smooth, snug collar fit, to see that armholes are roomy enough, that the length is correct and that it is becoming to you.

Usually products have some qualities that are plainly seen and some that are hidden. For example, you can look at a suit and find out if it is evenly stitched and has seams that are wide enough so they won't pull out, and so forth. But only a label can assure you that the material will not fade or shrink.

Not all clothes and fabrics carry labels telling what fibers they contain and giving advice on methods for care. They should do so, however. Today there is more and more insistence on good labeling.

An ideal label should tell the name of the manufacturer or sponsor of the product, of what it is made and possibly how it is made, the results of laboratory tests which show what service you may expect, directions for use and how to care for the article. Good labels help you with your buying and cut down on waste by giving you pointers on care and use. Whenever possible find and read labels and follow their instructions.

Color is given to cloth by dyeing either the fibers, the yarns or the finished cloth. When you are shopping, however, you will not find very much information about how the fabric was dyed or what dyes were used. But a label may tell you under what conditions the color is fast. Try to find out if cloth is colorfast to light, humidity, perspiration, crocking (color rubbing off) or washing. No color is permanent. But it is possible to find colors that will last throughout the life of the fabric.

Various printing methods are used in applying designs to fabrics, but the most popular printing for mass production is roller printing. This is done by engraving the design on copper rollers, using a separate roller for each color. Fabric is fed through the rollers in quick succession so that thousands of yards may be printed very fast. Usually only one side of the cloth is printed.

When you are buying patterned material, think of the size of the design in relation to your size. Remember, great masterpieces of painting use bright colors sparingly. Try to imagine the fabric against the background where you will wear it. Will the color be harmonious? Will the design be pleasing after several wearings?

But whatever you buy, be sure to give it proper care.

Develop the helpful habit of putting clothes on hangers right after wearing. Close buttons and zippers and ease the shoulders into place carefully. Fold sweaters carefully and lay them flat: hanging may stretch them.

Brushing sturdy fabrics with a medium-soft brush—brushing with the grain of the fabric—will cut down on trips to the laundry and the cleaner.

Change or protect your clothes to avoid spots when you are working or playing where spotting is likely. When clothing does get spotted, remove the spots with soap and water or a nonflammable cleaning fluid. But never try to do dry cleaning by immersion of the whole garment at home. It is usually a dangerous fire hazard and is almost never satisfactory.

14: OUR CHEMICAL AGE

THOUSANDS of years ago, man learned to make his very first tools out of stone and in that way began his long struggle toward a better way of life. Because stone was so important to human progress, we call that period the Stone Age.

Today, when the great science of chemistry is making such vast changes in our lives and in our industry, our age is often called the chemical age.

The textile revolution, which began when scientists at last learned how to create fibers chemically, has made it possible for millions of people to own more, better-fitting, more-useful and more-attractive clothes than ever before. Yet, thanks in part to man-made fibers, the portion of the average American budget which is spent for clothes has gone down and down. This is an excellent example of how scientific discovery and invention help man in his constant search for better ways of life for all.

But clothes are, of course, only a small part of the

picture. Though man-made fibers are still so new, scarcely a conveyor belt moves or a tire rolls without their aid. This one section of the chemical industry alone already keeps many huge factories busy and em-

ploys many thousands of workers. It is still growing and, like many other kinds of manufacturing in this chemical age, it will need more and more scientists and technicians.

In the search for better and cheaper fibers, hundreds of new compounds have been made in test-tube quantities—and the search goes on!

Chemistry's effect on the textile industry is of great importance, but many other products are being revolutionized, too. Paint, for example, had been made in the same old way for a very long time. Some was good, some not so good. And none would stand up against sun, heat, snow, rain and sleet for as long a time as men hoped they would. All outdoor paints would yellow and crack because their "binders" would oxidize. Then came the development of the silicones and their use in paint. Because the silicones are almost completely inert (chemically inactive) they stand up under the most difficult conditions. Today they are being used more and more widely, saving untold amounts in the cost of labor for repainting everything from dolls' carriages to things the size of San Francisco's Golden Gate Bridge.

Synthetic oil for your family automobile may soon be made from sand, coal and gases. It can last forty times as long as the petroleum-base oil we now use. The new oil won't become stiff and gummy, either, so starting the engine in cold weather will be no problem. Synthetic oil will be another one of the new products which belong to the family of silicones—a chemical relative of glass!

There are many other important silicones, too. One like rubber is used in jet-plane engines because it keeps its stretch even in Arctic cold and also can stand temperatures 250° higher than natural rubber or other synthetic rubbers. Thin, transparent liquid silicones sprayed on cotton cloth make it shed water as a plastic shower curtain does. Another silicone is used to glaze bakery bread pans. Once it is applied to a pan, for the next two hundred times that the pan is used the finished loaf of bread will drop out of it without the slightest bit of sticking.

Coal, to many of us, is something people used to burn before natural gas and the oil burner became so widely used for heating our houses. But coal is also the source of hundreds of chemicals. During World War II the Germans made 85 per cent of all their aviation gasoline out of coal. In recent years, Union Carbide, one of our big companies, has spent $20,000,000 in research and in building a plant to extract chemicals from coal. Some of the chemicals they got were so new that nobody knew how they might be used. But the company did not worry about that, for they knew that research would find a way to use them. Why were they so confident? Because they had been selling new chemicals at the rate of one new compound a month for twenty-five years! Think of it. One company alone had already introduced three hundred new chemicals before they built a new plant that was bound to produce dozens more! In the earliest tests of the products of Union Carbide's new plant, their chemists identified more than a hundred chemicals in the mixture of solids, liquids and gases that come from their coal process.

*   *   *

Are you interested in the vitally important chemistry of medicine? At least nine out of every ten prescriptions that doctors write today are for medicines that did not exist twenty years ago. The chemical age is adding years of health to the normal life span and promises to practically stamp out some of our worst diseases.

Here are just some of chemistry's exciting new discoveries: synthetic vanilla that cannot be distinguished from the natural; synthetic camphor purer than the most refined product of Japan's camphor trees; indigo from a chemical dye factory instead of from a growing plant; sulfa drugs; synthetic diamonds; a synthetic musk that is used as the base of many perfumes; adhesives with waterproof strength that our time-honored glue and paste never achieved. Each year there are nearly ten thousand new compounds made in our laboratories. And though many are never made for sale, some turn out to have dozens of uses that were never imagined when they were first made. Four of Union Carbide's chemicals which were of no use when first made in quantity have recently been selling at the rate of more than two billion pounds a year.

Hydrazine, which is made from ammonia, chlorine and caustic soda, looks like water and smells somewhat like ammonia. For years it was only a curiosity of the chemical laboratory. Nobody used it for anything. Then in World War II the Germans made it into a powerful fuel for their rockets. Today it is being used to make many things. Among them are a new drug against tuberculosis, another to reduce high blood pressure, a third which fights certain infections and still another which wars against a serious poultry disease —coccidiosis.

One chemical which is also made from hydrazine appeals to millions of boys and men. It is a spray for lawns which will make the grass stop growing at its usual fast rate and will save countless hours of mowing! More chemicals based on this one-time laboratory curiosity keep potatoes, onions, carrots, beets and turnips from sprouting for a whole year while in storage. One new chemical is used to make the millions of tiny bubbles in crepe rubber for the soles of shoes. Still others prevent rust in soldering automobile radiators, and guard against corrosion when they are added to water in the boilers of steam power plants.

Dozens of chemicals which are used in farming today were completely unknown until very recently. And more are being field-tested and eventually sold every year.

The bug killers, weed killers, growth regulators of growing plants and other chemical assistants have already cut down the farmer's task and have increased his production. New chemicals are sure to add to the world's food supply, and there is hope that some day no one anywhere need be hungry.

Today the production of textile fibers has become the biggest job in the vast chemical industry. Yet research in other kinds of chemistry may prove to be the key to tremendous new growth and development in other important fields. For our chemical age is an age of opportunity and promise.

If you are interested in science, chemistry may be the profession in which you can make a real contribution toward your fellow-man. If you should choose this very exacting, yet highly rewarding career, you will join an illustrious company of men and women.

For in the entire history of the progress of man, there is probably no more inspiring chapter than that in which scientists, by means of the amazing tool of chemistry, have found a way to gain greater and greater control over nature.

JUDGING FABRICS

Here are some of the things textile scientists have to think about in judging the value of any fiber or fabric, new or old:

abrasion
absorption
allergens
appearance
bacteria
bulk
chemical inertness
cleaning
crease holding
crease resistance
dyeing
electrical properties
feeling

fire resistance or
  flammability
fungus resistance
heat sensitivity
insulating quality—heat; electrical
mildew
printing
shrinkage control
static electricity
tensile strength—dry; wet
weight
wrinkle resistance

MAN-MADE FIBERS

**From
Natural "Giant" Molecules**

Cellulose Base
Rayon (Regenerated Cellulose)
  Viscose
  Cuprammonium
  Saponified Cellulose Acetate
Estron (Cellulose Esters)
  Cellulose Acetate
  Ethyl Cellulose (Experimental)
  Cellulose Acetate Butyrate (Experimental)

Protein Base
Azlon
  Milk Casein (Lanital—Italy)
Polyurethanes
  Perlon U (Germany)
  Polulan (Japan)
Polyvinyl Alcohol (Modified)
  Vinylon

Peanut (Ardil)
Corn (Vicara)

**From
Synthetic "Giant" Molecules**

Polyamides
  Nylon
  Perlon L (Germany)
  Amilan (Japan)
Polyacrylonitrile
  Orlon
Acrylonitrile—Vinyl Chloride
  Vinyon
  Dynel
Terphthalic Acid-Ethylene Glycol
  Terylene (England)
  Dacron
Polystyrene
Polyvinylidene Chloride
  Saran
Acrylonitrile-Vinyl Acetate
  Acrilan

GLOSSARY

Abrasion—wearing away of material by action similar to sandpapering.

Absorption—taking in of water; wool absorbs 20 per cent of its own weight in water without feeling wet, while fiber glass absorbs practically no water at all.

Allergens—substances causing allergies or irritations of the skin or other membranes of the human body. Certain oils, resins used in finishing fabrics sometimes have allergic effects.

Bleaching—removing unwanted coloring matter in fibers, yarns or fabrics by exposure to the sun or by chemical bleaching agents. Bleaching is usually done to get a white or a uniform color in natural fibers before dyeing.

Blending—two or more fibers mixed together and spun into a single yarn (see mixed fibers).

Carding—a type of combing to remove foreign matter from natural fibers and to bring them roughly into parallel.

Crease or crush resistance—ability of fabric to retain or recover its original appearance after hard wear, packing in a suitcase or other compressing treatment.

Crocking—rubbing off of color from dyed or printed fabric.

Dyeing—"stock-dyed" fabrics are made from fibers dyed before being spun into yarn.
"yarn-dyed" fabrics are those made from yarns dyed before weaving.
"piece-dyed" fabrics are those dyed after weaving.

Felt—dense, firm material made by pressing fibers together. Usually refers to wool alone or with hair or fur fibers. Tiny scales of wool fibers, when subjected to heat, moisture and pressure, interlock permanently.

Finishing—processing after weaving; included are processes to give fabrics a little nap or a lot; to give them a harder surface without obscuring the weave structure (as in tweed) or a treatment that is designed to obscure the weave structure as in broadcloth, velour or fleece. Other processes are mercerizing, water or moth-resistance treatments, etc.

Fulling—compressing newly woven cloth by moistening in warm water and passing between rollers under pressure; with loosely woven woolens, this process will intentionally shrink the fabric from 10 to 30 per cent depending on the weave structure and the severity of the fulling treatment.

Hand—the feeling of a fabric to the hand or against the skin. A "warm, dry hand" is a phrase used to describe the feeling of an angora or a cashmere sweater, for example.

Lisle—a cotton yarn in which two or more yarns are twisted tightly together and then passed through flame to produce a fine, smooth yarn.

Long staple—cotton fibers of one and one-eighth to two inches in length. Sea Island, Egyptian and Pima are among the longest.

Mercerized—mercerized cotton has more luster and, when properly done, has greater strength than untreated fabric. In the process the fibers or fabric are immersed in strong, cold caustic soda under tension for a few minutes, removed, washed, neutralized and dried under tension.

Mixed fibers—weaving together of two or more yarns of different kinds of fibers such as wool and Dacron, cotton and linen.

Napping—method of pulling the ends of fibers to the surface of a woven fabric, producing a fuzzy or downy face and feeling.

Resilience—elasticity; ability of fiber or fabric to recover size and shape after strain and deforming; see Chapter XIII—"Which Shall I Choose?"

Slip resistance—a chemical finishing method that is sometimes used to prevent yarns of a woven fabric from slipping out of place.

Spinning—the process of drawing out and twisting fibers into a yarn. This term also applies to the process of the silkworm when he spins his cocoon around himself. (See chapter on silk.)

Warp—the lengthwise yarns of a woven fabric. On modern looms they are fed from drums that often carry enough yarn to make 10,000 yards of fabric.

Water repellent—term used to describe natural ability to shed water or chemical treatment of a fabric to give it that ability. Some treatments will withstand either washing or dry cleaning. Others must be renewed.

Weft—the filling yarns that cross and recross the warp threads of a woven fabric. Also called the woof.

Woolens—fabrics made from woolen yarns which are spun from short fibers and criss-crossed in every direction during the spinning. Woolens are softer and fuzzier than worsteds.

Worsted—(pronounced *woosted,* oo as in wool) yarn made of long, fine wool fibers, carefully combed and treated to remove all short, broken and imperfect fibers; yarn is spun so that all fibers lie smooth and parallel. Fabrics of worsted are smooth and can be clear and crisp as worsted gabardine or with a napped surface like most men's suits.